Secrets to Successful Events Resource Guide

42+ Easy-to-Use Forms and Tools to Save You Time and Money

Lynn Fuhler

Flying Compass Press
Winston-Salem, North Carolina

Flying Compass Press
P.O. Box 24305
Winston-Salem, North Carolina 27114

Copyright ©2016 by Lynn Fuhler. All rights reserved.

First edition.

The Flying Compass logo is a registered mark of Flying Compass, Inc.

For information about special discounts for bulk purchases, please contact:
Flying Compass Press, P.O. Box 24305, Winston-Salem, NC 27114 or publisher@flyingcompass.com.

Manufactured in the United States of America.

Publisher's Cataloging-in-Publication
(Provided by Quality Books, Inc.)

Fuhler, Lynn, author.
    Secrets to successful events resource guide : 42+
easy-to-use forms and tools to save you time and money /
Lynn Fuhler. -- First edition.
    pages cm
    LCCN 2016962980
    ISBN-13: 978-0-9979807-2-1 (pbk.)
    ISBN-10: 0-9979807-2-9 (pbk.)

    1. Special events--Planning--Handbooks, manuals, etc.
2. Special events--Management--Handbooks, manuals, etc.
3. Meetings--Planning--Handbooks, manuals, etc.
4. Congresses and conventions--Planning--Handbooks,
manuals, etc. 5. Special events industry--Vocational
guidance--Handbooks, manuals, etc. 6. Handbooks and
manuals.   I. Title.

GT3405.F842 2017   394.2068
                    QBI17-900002

Contents

To Steve & The Boys

Preface

Numerous sample letters, agreements, tools and forms were planned to be included in my first book *Secrets to Successful Events: How to Organize, Promote and Manage Exceptional Events and Festivals* (The Book). However, in order to make it available in digital format, the decision was made to pull out these materials and, instead, to create two separate books. Unfortunately, forms do not always display properly and consistently in the various size eBooks - smartphones, tablets and laptops. To give readers an optimum experience, *Secrets to Successful Events Resource Guide: 42+ Easy-to-Use Forms and Tools to Save You Time and Money* (Resource Guide) is currently only available in print.

The Book explains "what" an event organizer needs to do to create a successful event and in many cases details "how" to do it, too. The Resource Guide goes a step further. It provides helpful communication tools to save event and festival planners time, energy and money.

Everyone's experiences, skills, talents and knowledge base differ including event planners. For those who want to know *everything* about organizing an event, they may wish to pick up a copy of The Book and the Resource Guide.

For instance, a Committee Vice Chairman may be well-versed on the inner workings of a few areas of the event. To prepare to become the Event or Festival Chairman, this individual may desire to gain a comprehensive understanding of the entire event to see how all the pieces fit together.

For those wondering if their event contracts and agreements with sponsors, talent and concessions/vendors cover everything, the Resource Guide may be a worthwhile read. Those desiring to fine tune an existing event may want to explore The Book from cover-to-cover or focus on specific chapters.

How many of you discovered too late that the now Past Chairman elected not to share his or her files, maintained minimal records or left nothing but useless information behind? In these situations, the Resource Guide can be extremely helpful, providing working documents to customize.

The Resource Guide makes a great starter set for someone who has event experience but neither the time nor interest to create the various communication tools nor the desire or funds to employ someone to draft contracts and agreements who isn't familiar with event and festival management.

Introduction

Organized in a logical progression, the *Secrets to Successful Events Resource Guide: 42+ Easy-to-Use Forms and Tools to Save You Time and Money* (Resource Guide) follows the same sequence as *Secrets to Successful Events: How to Organize, Promote and Manage Exceptional Events and Festivals* (The Book). First-time event planners will discover how well the contents of the Resource Guide dovetail with The Book. Together these two publications provide a complete how-to manual for executing an event from start-to-finish and beyond. Seasoned event professionals may elect to pick up the Resource Guide with its full range of communication tools rather than starting a new event from the ground up.

It's all here - a diagram of the event's committees showing who reports to whom as well as policies and procedures that address basic housekeeping matters like how to pay bills and who can speak to the media. You'll also find everything you'll need to solicit potential sponsors, lock in their sponsorships and how best to follow-up with them to assure they receive maximum exposure and will return year after year.

Much is involved in establishing an event budget and the Resource Guide provides insight into revenue streams, like merchandise and concessions/vendors, and the types of potential expenses an Event Chairman and Treasurer can expect to encounter.

The devil is in the details when it comes to marketing and PR. Key tools, some often overlooked, will help you get started. Booking talent - headliners, artists, speakers, musicians, pilots, performers, winemakers, authors, chefs, entertainers and brewmasters - and coordinating travel and equipment arrangements requires a well documented paper trail. It's conveniently provided for you to get a running start.

The foundation of any great event is the army of volunteers who devote countless hours to make it happen. We've organized it to make it easier.

Soliciting vendors to provide services, such as sound and lighting, creative design, and merchandise like tee shirts and posters, is much more convenient if you can use or modify an existing request for proposal (RFP) form. Food and beverage concessions/vendors can add a new dimension to any event. Similar to booking talent, it's important to consistently communicate and document the process in order that no surprises pop up during the event.

As your function draws to a close and you return to your everyday activities, you can breath a sigh of relief knowing thank-you letters have been written. All you need to do is customize them to your event.

For your convenience, every chapter's title is found on the top of each page.

The Organizational Chart

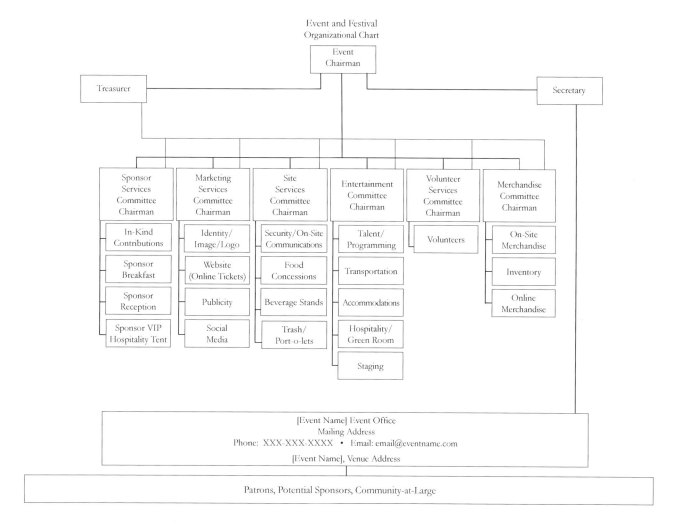

Policies and Procedures

[Event Name]
Policies and Procedures

FINANCES

BUDGETS

All Organizing Committee Chairmen, working with their committees, will submit their respective budgets at the [Month Date] meeting. These budgets shall include a detailed breakdown of all anticipated revenue and expenses for this fiscal year.

The budgets will then be reviewed, revised and approved by the Event Chairman and Treasurer. Approved and/or adjusted budgets will then be returned to the respective Committee Chairmen.

Careful attention to these working budgets is essential:

1.   Non-budgeted items will need the prior written approval of the Event Chairman and Treasurer and result in the reduction of other budgeted committee line items.

2.   When an expense significantly varies from the actual budget, adjustments to the entire [Event Name] budget may be necessary.

Budget variations in excess of $X,XXX will need the approval of the Event Chairman and Treasurer in advance.

ENTERTAINMENT BUDGET

At the direction of the Entertainment Committee Chairman, the Talent/Programming Coordinator will be requested to obtain information regarding the talent, for example, compatibility with the event format, prices, date availability, etc. The committee will not be authorized to request contracts until after budgets have been approved. Once budgets have been approved and sponsorship support in hand, and only then, will the Talent/Programming Coordinator be permitted to request a contract or initiate a contract.

INVOICES

The Treasurer will need to prepare all sponsorship invoices. The Sponsor Services Committee Chairman will need to work with the Treasurer to assure timely processing.

CHECK REQUISITIONS

Committee Chairmen shall be responsible for submitting their committee's check requisitions. See Check Requisition.

All invoices submitted by the 15th of the month will be paid by the 30th of the month and all invoices submitted by the 30th of the month will be paid by the 15th of the following month. All check requisitions shall be accompanied by an original invoice or supporting documentation. Please send information to the Treasurer's email address or bring it to the next committee meeting. It is suggested that the originators keep a copy of the invoice or back up materials and requisition form in the committee's file.

Checks should require dual signatures, that of the Treasurer, Event Chairman and/or Immediate Past Chairman. A check written to one of the above individuals will need the signature of the other.

There can be no exception to this policy.

REQUESTS FOR PROPOSALS/BIDS
In an effort to assure the [Event Name] is a true community event, it is suggested each Committee Chairman secure at least three bids for those items costing $X,XXX or more. These should then be submitted to the Event Chairman with a recommendation. Quality, price and ability to perform or deliver in a timely fashion should be considered before awarding a bid. If a bid is selected that is not the lowest price, please be prepared to discuss why.

ASSETS
[Event Name] materials have been stored at ZYS [building name and address]. Should a Committee Chairman need to access this area, please contact the Site Services Committee Chairman to make arrangements to sign out and pick up the keys to the storage facility. On behalf of the Treasurer, the Secretary or Administrative Assistant maintains the storage facility inventory. Please provide an update if items are removed, returned, damaged or destroyed.

COMMUNICATION

COMMITTEE COMMUNICATIONS
Please use email for all internal communication. Please start the subject line with the first two letters of the first two words of the event. This will help in locating them amid many emails. If at all possible, include your committee name and a single word subject next.

When sending emails, please copy each affected Committee Chairman as well as the Event Chairman and the Secretary or Administrative Assistant for the office. With respect to those items that are budgetary in nature, please also copy the Treasurer.

All [Event Name] email accounts shall include an electronic signature including the sender's name, committee name and title, event logo, social media icons and links, the mailing address, event phone number and the sender's direct phone number. The Marketing Services Committee shall provide to each Organizing Committee member the signature complete with logo, social media icons and standard copy in the appropriate font style with directions how to install.

EXTERNAL COMMUNICATION
Official [Event Name] letterhead or a digital letterhead template will be provided to Committee Chairmen. It is recommended this be used for sponsor, concession/vendor, publicity purposes and other formal external communication. The template will be pre-set with the standard font and type size.

The Event Chairman will need to review and approval all external correspondence prior to mass distribution.

All [Event Name] outbound communication should include the sender's name, committee name and title and the senders' direct phone number. Please copy the Secretary or Administrative Assistant for the (virtual) office files.

All [Event Name] collateral materials created by the Marketing Services Committee should include the mailing address, venue/location address, website address and event telephone number, including area code.

CONFIDENTIAL MATTERS
Since the [Event Name] is an organization to which many matters of confidential nature are entrusted, each Organizing Committee member must keep in strictest confidence any sensitive information acquired and be generally discreet as to matters handled by the event.

AUTHORIZED SPOKESPERSON

The Event Chairman shall be designated the official spokesperson for all media communication for the event as well as for related events, should any occur. Please refer all media inquiries to the Public Relations and Publicity Committee Chairman. The Event Chairman may call upon members of the Organizing Committee from time to time to handle select interviews confined to their respective areas. This policy is designed to ensure uniformity.

MAIL

INCOMING

The [Event Name] has secured a post office box at XYZ location and the [Event Name] has three keys. These will be held by the Secretary or Administrative Assistant and the Treasurer and may be assigned to a Committee Chairman expecting a response to an activity.

This box will be checked for incoming mail at least twice per week. Please advise the Secretary or Administrative Assistant or the Treasurer if you are expecting important mail.

Interoffice envelopes will be purchased to conveniently move mail to the appropriate party.

OUTGOING

A bulk mail permit number has been offered to the Organizing Committee for U.S. postal mailings of identical pieces meeting the minimum requirement. Contact the Marketing Services Committee Chairman for details. Committees are encouraged to utilize this method if mass mailings are scheduled.

LOGO

The official [Event Name] logo may be available to the various Committee Chairmen upon written request and approval of the Marketing Services Committee Chairman. This same committee can assist with logo specifications such as color, resolution, file formats, etc.

Anyone wishing to utilize the logo will be advised in writing that the logo and words [Event Name] are the registered service mark of the event and any use thereof without written permission is strictly forbidden.

SPONSORSHIP

All sponsors will be given the courtesy of a formal presentation. No self-presentations shall be permitted by any Organizing Committee member on behalf of the event. The Event Chairman and the Sponsor Services Committee Chairman will need to be advised more than 48 hours in advance that a meeting is being planned with a potential sponsor. Each sponsor call will be made with at least two event representatives being present. For the purpose of continuity, it is recommended these two consist of at least the Event Chairman or Sponsor Services Committee Chairman or Immediate Past Chairman.

SPONSOR CATEGORIES

The following are sponsorship categories: Major Sponsors and Contributing Sponsors.

The following are underwriting categories: Underwriter, Patron and Friend.

To assure parity within established sponsorship categories, no categories or packages shall be created or modified other than those noted above.

PACKAGE CONTENT
The Event Chairman, the Immediate Past Chairman and the Sponsor Services Committee Chairman shall review the contents of each level of sponsorship each year. No changes or adjustment shall be made without the approval of this group. In-kind sponsors will be requested to provide supporting documentation of value of products and services provided.

SPONSOR COMMUNICATION
All correspondence with sponsors shall be copied to the Event Chairman and the Sponsor Services Committee Chairman. A written report shall be submitted by the Sponsor Services Committee Chairman at each Organizing Committee meeting updating the status of sponsorship calls.

SPONSORSHIP AGREEMENTS
The original agreement should be provided to the Treasurer along with payment in full, if applicable. Copies of fully executed contracts should be provided to the Event Chairman, kept on file by the Sponsor Services Committee Chairman and marketing relevant details of the agreement provided to the Marketing Services Committee Chairman.

SPONSOR INVOICES
Following the signing of the agreement by the Event Chairman, the Sponsor Services Committee Chairman will provide a fully executed agreement to the sponsor along with a thank-you letter. Within 30 days an invoice will be generated by the Treasurer and sent requesting funds. Upon the request of a sponsor, billings can be provided on a monthly or quarterly basis.

THE COMMITTEE

MEETINGS
Organizing Committee meetings will be held at XYZ [building name and address]. A full schedule of meeting dates will be distributed at the first meeting. In some instances, it may be more appropriate for the Event Chairman to hold a meeting with a select group of Committee Chairmen versus the full Organizing Committee. Appropriate notification will be given.

COMMITTEE MEETINGS
Committee Chairmen may call meetings of their respective committees as necessary. Committee meetings are encouraged.

MEETING NOTICES, AGENDAS and MINUTES
The Secretary or Administrative Assistant will provide notice of meetings, agendas and minutes to members of the full Organizing Committee prior to each meeting.

ORGANIZATIONAL STRUCTURE
See The Organizational Chart.

[EVENT NAME] ORGANIZING COMMITTEE
CHAIRMAN
The [Event Name] Chairman, selected by [an individual's name who, or the organization that, appoints the Event Chairman], oversees the day-to-day planning and operation of the annual event and is given the authority and responsibility by the ABC hosting or presenting organization to execute the event. The Event Chairman's term of office shall begin on [Month Date] of each year and end on [Month Date, less one day] of the following year. The Event Chairman shall be encouraged to select a Vice Chairman to assist in the overall responsibilities. If a rising position, the Vice Chairman shall become the Event Chairman the following year.

The Event Chairman appoints individuals to oversee various functions including Committee Chairmen. These Committee Chairmen may appoint various committee members in consultation with the Event Chairman.

The Event Chairman has the authority to remove any Committee Chairman for violating any of the policies stated herein. Failing to comply with reasonable requests by the Event Chairman is also grounds for dismissal.

The Organizing Committee is responsible for the organizing and presenting of the annual [Event Name]. The Organizing Committee provides the day-to-day planning and execution of the event. Organizing Committee members are expected to attend all X-days of the event, plus be present on set-up and tear-down days.

ORGANIZING COMMITTEE
Positions on the Organizing Committee and their respective position titles are for one year beginning on [Month Date] and end on [Month Date, less one day] of the following year. A copy of all materials developed to execute the event shall be turned in on [Month Date] and/or placed in storage or be available for use by the next year's Organizing Committee.

ORGANIZING COMMITTEE RELATIONSHIP with PRESENTING ORGANIZATION
Please invite representatives of the hosting or presenting organization to various events. This will be part of the Sponsor Services Committee's area of responsibility.

Check Requisition

[Event Name]
Check Requisition Form

Make check payable to the following:

Name: _____

Address: _____

City: _____ State: _____ Zip Code: _____

Committee Name: _____

Purpose: _____

Charge to budget line item #: _____

This has been authorized by: _____

Submitted by: _____   _____
                           Print Name   Signature

Total Amount: _____ Due Date: _____

1. Please include the original receipt or invoice. Please keep a copy of the receipt or invoice for your records along with a copy of this completed check requisition form.

2. Please submit these using one of the following methods: a) scan and email as a PDF attachment to: treasurer@eventdomainname.com; b) submit to the Treasurer at the next Organizing Committee meeting; or c) send via U.S. mail to: Treasurer; [Event Name], [Mailing Address, City and Zip Code].

3. All invoices submitted by the 15th of the month will be paid by the 30th of the month and all invoices submitted by the 30th of the month will be paid by the 15th of the following month. All check requisitions shall be accompanied by an original invoice or supporting documentation.

4. In the event your purchase includes warranty information, please bring this information to the next Organizing Committee meeting for the Secretary or Administrative Assistant to file.

5. If the value of your purchase exceeds $XXX, it should be logged in the inventory control system. Please ask the Secretary or Administrative Assistant to enter it into the event's list of assets and indicate where the item is stored so it can be tagged: "Property of [Event Name]."

Thank you.

Sponsorship Package - Major Sponsor

Xth Annual [Event Name]
Event Dates: [Month Date to Date, 20XX]
Major Sponsor
$XX,XXX Sponsorship Package

ADVERTISING

The Sponsor name and/or logo will appear in all promotional pieces promoting the [Event Name].

The Sponsor logo will be placed in a prominent position on the current year's [Event Name] poster.

The Sponsor will receive one complimentary full page/panel color advertisement in the annual [Event Name] brochure, program or schedule. These marketing materials will be:

- Mailed in response to year-round requests for information,

- Provided to Sponsor for distribution at their business locations,

- Included in the local economic development agency's business relocation packets, and

- Distributed at the sponsor's booth during the event.

A downloadable PDF of the brochure, program or schedule will be available on the [Event Name] website.

The Sponsor's corporate bio will be featured in the brochure, program or schedule.

Optional radio and newspaper advertising packages promoting the [Event Name] are available through WXXX or KXXX and through the Newspaper Sponsor for the [Event Name] special section or tabloid.

ON-SITE EXPOSURE

Banners with the Sponsor name and/or logo will be displayed at the [Venue/Location] during the event. Sponsors are requested to provide the [Event Name] with X+ banners.

The Sponsor logo will be prominently displayed on a large banner over the main stage area during the X-day event.

The Sponsor logo and/or name will be featured in prerecorded commercials played during intermission on large screens at the venue or announced by on-air personalities from the stage throughout the event.

A Sponsor representative will be asked to participate in a minimum of X+ on-stage presentations which will recognize the corporation as a major sponsor.

The Sponsor will have access to the VIP seating area directly in front of the main stage area during the event.

HOSPITALITY

The Sponsor will receive invitations to a Sponsor Breakfast which honors the Sponsors and incorporates the unveiling of the current year's [Event Name] poster. Media are invited to attend.

The Sponsor will receive X+ VIP credentials providing access to the event and X+ VIP parking passes.

The Sponsor will receive X+ framed [Event Name] commemorative posters.

The Sponsor will receive Y+ unframed [Event Name] commemorative posters.

The Sponsor will receive X [Event Name] tee shirts with its corporate logo imprinted on the back.

The Sponsor will receive special discounted rates on group tee shirts ordered prior to the event.

The Sponsor will receive invitations to the annual [Event Name] Kick-Off Party.

The Sponsor is invited to enjoy other related events.

The Sponsor will receive invitations to the Sponsor Reception honoring the [current year] corporate sponsors.

A special rate or complimentary hotel accommodations may be provided for the major sponsors subject to availability.

PUBLICITY

The Sponsor will be recognized as a major sponsor of the Xth Annual [Event Name] in all news releases sent to local, regional, state, national, international and travel publications.

The Sponsor will be recognized in a proclamation issued by City Hall and presented to the event.

SOCIAL MEDIA

Before, during and after [Event Name], the event will utilize social media to gain additional exposure for its sponsors using various networks or platforms such as Twitter.

Sponsorship Package - Contributing Sponsor

Xth Annual [Event Name]
Event Dates: [Month Date to Date, 20XX]
Contributing Sponsor
$XX,XXX Sponsorship Package

ADVERTISING

The Sponsor name will appear in promotional pieces promoting the [Event Name].

The Sponsor name will be placed on the current year's [Event Name] poster.

The Sponsor will receive one complimentary half-page/panel black and white advertisement in the annual [Event Name] brochure, program or schedule. These marketing materials will be:

- Mailed in response to year-round requests for information,

- Provided to Sponsor for distribution at their business locations,

- Included in the local economic development agency's business relocation packets, and

- Distributed at the sponsor's booth during the event.

A downloadable PDF of the brochure, program or schedule will be available on the [Event Name] website.

Optional radio and newspaper advertising packages promoting the [Event Name] are available through WXXX or KXXX and through the Newspaper Sponsor for the [Event Name] special section or tabloid.

ON-SITE EXPOSURE

Banners with the Sponsor name and/or logo will be displayed at the [Venue/Location] during the event. Sponsors are requested to provide the [Event Name] with X banners.

The Sponsor name will be prominently displayed on a large banner over the main stage area during the X-day event.

The Sponsor name will be mentioned during intermission by on-air personalities from the stage throughout the event.

A Sponsor representative will be asked to participate in X on-stage presentations which will recognize the corporation as a contributing sponsor.

The Sponsor will have access to VIP seating directly in front of the main stage area during the event.

HOSPITALITY

The Sponsor will receive invitations to a Sponsor Breakfast which honors the Sponsors and incorporates the unveiling of the current year's [Event Name] poster. Media are invited to attend.

The Sponsor will receive X VIP credentials providing access to the event and X VIP parking passes.

The Sponsor will receive X framed [Event Name] commemorative posters.

The Sponsor will receive Y unframed [Event Name] commemorative posters.

The Sponsor will receive special discounted rates on group tee shirts ordered prior to the event.

The Sponsor will receive invitations to the annual [Event Name] Kick-Off Party.

The Sponsor is invited to enjoy other related events.

The Sponsor will receive invitations to the Sponsor Reception honoring the [current year] corporate sponsors.

PUBLICITY

The Sponsor will be recognized as a contributing sponsor of the Xth Annual [Event Name] in all news releases sent to local, regional, state, national, international and travel publications.

SOCIAL MEDIA

Before, during and after [Event Name], the event will utilize social media to gain additional exposure for its sponsors using various networks or platforms such as Twitter.

Sponsorship Agreement

Xth Annual [Event Name]
[Type, Level, Category] Sponsorship Agreement

This agreement is made and effective this _____ day of _____, 20 _____ by and between the [Event Full Legal Name], DBA hereinafter referred to as the Event and _____ hereinafter known as the Sponsor.

Whereas, the Event will be producing the Xth Annual [Event Name] to be held in [Venue/Location] on [Month Date to Date, 20XX].

Whereas, the Sponsor has agreed to support the Event by contributing funds to the Event for use in this project.

Now, therefore, in consideration of the mutual promises and agreements herein contained, and for other good and valuable consideration, the parties hereby agree as follows:

1. The Sponsor agrees to act as a [Type, Level, Category] sponsor for the Xth Annual [Event Name] by contributing the amount of $ _____ and the Event agrees to accept the goods and services.

2. The Event agrees to promote the participation of the Sponsor as outlined in the attached Sponsorship Package Addendum.

3. The Sponsor agrees the services promised will be performed in a timely manner.

4. The Sponsor understands and agrees that substantially all of the products, goods and services which it has agreed to contribute will be provided for use in conducting a quality event, and all of the like services and materials contributed will be non-refundable, if for any reason, such as inclement weather or civil unrest, the Event is canceled in whole or part. The Sponsor hereby agrees to release the Event from any obligation to refund all or any portion of the Sponsor's contribution.

_____
                Date

[Event Full Legal Name]

By: _____
Signature

_____
Sponsor Name (please type or print)

_____
Authorized Representative Title

_____
Signature

_____
Representative's Name and Title (please type or print)

_____
Mailing Address

_____

City, State and Zip Code

_____

Direct Phone Number: (For event internal use only)

Sponsorship Invoice

Note: Place the invoice on the [Event Name] letterhead. The mailing address for the sponsor may be different than the physical address of the sponsor. The Sponsor Services Committee Chairman should verify this before requesting the Treasurer prepare an invoice.

Invoice No.

[Month Date, 20XX]

[Contact Person and Title]
[Company Name]
[Mailing Address]
[City, State and Zip Code]

[List the year of the event] [Event Name] and [Type, Level, Category] of sponsorship.

[List the dollar amount followed by a decimal point and indicated cents, even if zeros.]

Make checks payable to: [Full Legal Event Name]
                               [Mailing Address]
                               [City, State and Zip Code]

Due and payable upon receipt.

Sponsor Checklist

Xth Annual [Event Name]
Event Dates: [Month Date to Date, 20XX]

Major Sponsor Checklist*
*Note: The Contributing Sponsor Checklist will be similar but adjustments will need to be made for quantities and content.

CORPORATE TITLE
Please use the following as our complete and correct title when referring to our organization:

_____

1. Social Media Address: _____

2. Social Media Address:_____

3. Social Media Address: _____

PRE EVENT
CORPORATE BIOGRAPHY
Please provide a 30-50 word description of your organization for use in the current year's [Event Name] brochure, program or schedule. Copy provided in excess of the requested length will be edited at the event's discretion. This piece will be distributed to event inquiries, to tourism and economic development inquiries, and during the event. The [Event Name] will provide brochures, programs or schedules to your corporation for distribution to your customers, clients and employees. A downloadable PDF of the brochure, program or schedule will be available on the [Event Name] website: http://www.eventdomainname.com.

Deadline: On or before [Day of the Week, Month Date, 20XX].

BROCHURE, PROGRAM or SCHEDULE ADVERTISING
Please provide a high resolution, full panel, print ready PDF ad in the following dimension:
        Bleed size: 3.75" wide x 8.75" high
        Trim size: 3.25" wide x 8.25" high

Should you desire to receive a copy of last year's brochure, program or schedule, please let us know. Please see contact information on the last page of this checklist.

If you are a returning sponsor, please let us know if the ad is a pick-up from the prior year. Please see contact information on the last page of this checklist.

Deadline: On or before [Day of the Week, Month Date, 20XX].

YOUR CORPORATE LOGO
Please provide us your high resolution, 4-color logo in editable .eps format. This will provide the event the greatest flexibility. Should your organization have a brand standards specifications sheet with 4-color, PMS and hex colors,

please provide so we can assure your corporate identity is accurately represented. Please see contact information on the last page of this checklist.

The logo will be placed in the brochure, program or schedule, and on the poster, corporate banner, website and in all advertising.

Deadline: On or before [Day of the Week, Month Date, 20XX].

[EVENT NAME] LOGO

The [Event Name] will provide to your corporation a high resolution, 4-color logo in .eps format, as well as the approved brand standards for one and two color projects. Immediately below the [Event Name] logo, please position in Gill Sans® Pro Light 11 type font, the following text: "Proud Sponsor of the [Event Name]."

Deadline: On or before [Day of the Week, Month Date, 20XX].

NEWS RELEASES

Your corporate name will be included in all news releases promoting the event. Entertainment, features, travel and lifestyle editors will be targeted at local, state and national newspapers and magazines. News directors and assignment editors respectively will be the contacts at radio and television stations. A newswire distribution service will also be used.

A copy of each news release will be provided to the sponsor for possible inclusion in employee communications and social media posts.

CORPORATE COMMUNICATION

Event updates will be provided on a regular basis announcing details regarding talent, concessions/vendors, volunteers, the poster unveiling, etc. This information will be available for you to share with your employees and customers to promote your involvement with the event. Prior to and throughout the event, an [Event Name] photographer will be available to capture editorial photographs for use in your corporate publications, website and social media posts. These images will be added to the event's media website image library and be available for downloading. Password access will be provided to your corporation by the event. News releases can also be downloaded from the same media website.

SPONSOR BREAKFAST

X representatives from your organization will be invited to an exclusive Sponsor Breakfast honoring the current year's [Event Name] sponsors. Photos will be taken at this event and provided to your organization to be used in in-house and trade publications and on social media. Local media typically cover this event.

Anticipated Date: This event is usually held X months prior to the event on a [Day of the Week] and is hosted by our official hotel sponsor. Invitations will follow.

COMMEMORATIVE POSTER

During this exclusive Sponsor Breakfast, the current year's [Event Name] poster will be unveiled and poster presentations will occur. As a result of your support, your organization will receive X+ framed posters and Y+ unframed posters.

TEE SHIRTS

Your corporation will receive X complimentary [Event Name] tee shirts imprinted with your corporate logo. In addition, your corporation will receive special discounted rates on additional group tee shirts ordered prior to the event. Many corporations make these available to its employees volunteering at the event.

PRESALE OPPORTUNITIES at SPONSOR FACILITIES

To build pre-event enthusiasm, corporate sponsor facilities, offices, etc., can serve as pre-event sales outlets for popular [Event Name] merchandise. Customers, clients, employees and the community-at-large are invited to purchase [Event Name] souvenirs before the event occurs. The [Event Name] will announce to the media the various locations and times merchandise is available. Each corporate sponsor is eligible for X local locations and Y regional locations.

If you are interested, please advise by [Day of the Week, Month Date, 20XX]. Please see contact information on the last page of this checklist.

Deadline: On or before [Day of the Week, Month Date, 20XX].

COMMUNITY INVOLVEMENT

Each year more than X,XXX volunteer hours are needed to produce the [Event Name]. Your corporation's volunteers will have the opportunity to show their community spirit. A website link to a special online volunteer sign-up form will be provided. Our Volunteer Services Committee Chairman will work with your corporate representative to coordinate your employees' involvement.

AT THE EVENT

INDIVIDUAL BANNERS

Special areas have been preassigned to our corporate sponsors to maximize their exposure to the more than XXX,XXX visitors who enjoy the [Event Name]. Please provide the festival with X-6' wide x 4' high or smaller banners. The Sponsor Services Committee Chairman will return your organization's banners within two weeks following the event.

Because these banners will be outdoors for X-days and weather conditions can vary, we would suggest the banners have grommets in at least the four corners and cut-outs to allow air to flow through in case of heavy winds.

Please see contact information on the last page of this checklist.

Pick up or delivery deadline: On or before [Day of the Week, Month Date, 20XX].

SPONSOR RECEPTION

A special off-site, opening reception will be hosted by the [Event Name] to welcome you and open the festival. X representatives from your corporation and their spouse or guest will be invited and toasted during this causal event to be held at the official host hotel.

Anticipated Date: Opening Night, [Day of the Week, Month Date, 20XX]. Invitations will follow.

VENUE/LOCATION STAGE BANNER

Your corporation's logo will be prominently displayed on the [Event Name] banner which will be featured over the main stage area.

VIP PARKING

Your corporation will receive website links to X+ VIP parking passes per day to access a special VIP reserved parking area. A map with the location of the parking area will also be provided. Attendees will be required to present to the parking lot attendees their paper parking pass or QR code (displays on a smartphone).

Deadline: On or before [Day of the Week, Month Date, 20XX].

VIP CORPORATE SEATING

Your corporation will receive X+ VIP credentials providing access to a special VIP seating area directly in front of the main stage. Your corporate representative is encouraged to provide email addresses of key personnel or coordinate the registration of your corporation's attendees. When email addresses are provided a private invitation will be sent with the credentials. A waitlist feature will be available for peak demand days/times. Attendees will be required to present their VIP Seating paper ticket or QR code (displays on a smartphone) to gain entry.

Deadline: On or before [Day of the Week, Month Date, 20XX].

MERCHANDISE

The [Event Name] merchandise booth sells commemorative posters, tee shirts and other souvenir items. To package those items and to increase your visibility, the festival would welcome receiving up to X bags with your corporate logo imprinted.

Deadline: On or before [Day of the Week, Month Date, 20XX]. Please see contact information on the last page of this checklist.

VOLUNTEERS

The [Event Name] is a great opportunity for corporate volunteers to wear their corporate tee shirts. A website link to a special online volunteer sign-up form will be provided to you or your organization's volunteer contact. The event's Volunteer Services Committee Chairman will work with your corporate representative to coordinate your employees' involvement.

STAGE PRESENTATIONS

Your corporation will be given the opportunity to participate in stage presentations (1 on [Day of the Week], 1 on [Day of the Week], 2 on [Day of the Week] and 2 on [Day of the Week]). Prior to the event, your organization will be contacted and advised of the specific time of the presentations. Your corporation will also receive repeated mentions throughout the event from the stage. For scheduling purposes, it will be necessary to adhere to the presentation schedule once set.

Deadline: On or before [Day of the Week, Month Date, 20XX].

CORPORATE WEEKEND PACKAGE

To make your weekend more enjoyable, a special two-night/three-day getaway package has been reserved for your corporation. The [Event Name] is pleased to make reservations for your corporate representative. The [Venue/ Location] is just a short drive away during the day and at night your accommodations get you even closer to the related event sessions. A total of 2 rooms [Day of the Week, Month Date, 20XX] and 2 rooms [Day of the Week, Month Date, 20XX], will be provided. Please see contact information on the last page of this checklist.

Deadline: On or before [Day of the Week, Month Date, 20XX].

INFORMATION BOOTH

Your corporation collateral or advertising materials can be distributed throughout the X-day event at the information booth. Anticipate your needs based on XX,XXX attendees and X,XXX volunteers. Prior to the event, these promotional items will need to be reviewed and approved. Certain restrictions may apply.

The information booth also serves at the volunteer check-in area, lost and found, raffle headquarters and is where medical staff is housed throughout the event.

Deadline: On or before [Day of the Week, Month Date, 20XX].

POST EVENT

MEMORIES, MEMORIES, MEMORIES

To make sure you won't forget a single moment, the [Event Name] will photograph much of the event and will provide you snapshots and/or B-roll video of those special moments, along with usage rights.
Note: Audio recording of contracted talent without the express written permission in advance is strictly prohibited.

ADVERTISING

Your corporation's logo will be prominently displayed in a post-event acknowledgment of your support in the daily newspaper advertisement.

RELATED EVENT OPPORTUNITIES

Additional promotional opportunities may be available throughout the year.

[Event Name] CONTACT

Name: _____

[Event Name] Title: _____

Mailing Address: _____

City: _____ State: _____ Zip Code: _____

[Company Name] Title: _____

Physical Address: _____

City: _____   State: _____   Zip Code: _____

Mailing Address: _____

City: _____   State: _____   Zip Code: _____

Phone (Direct Line): _____   Email Address: _____

Best Day and Time to Contact: _____

Cell Phone: _____   Call between: _____ a.m./p.m. and _____ a.m./p.m.
☐ Text me using my cell number, if an emergency.

SPONSOR CONTACT

Name: _____

Title: _____

Physical Address: _____

City: _____   State: _____   Zip Code: _____

Mailing Address: _____

City: _____   State: _____   Zip Code: _____

Phone (Direct Line): _____   Email Address: _____

Best Day and Time to Contact: _____

Cell Phone: _____   Call between: _____ a.m./p.m. and _____ a.m./p.m.
☐ Text me using my cell number, if an emergency.

Alternate Contact Name: _____

Title: _____

Phone (Direct Line): _____   Email Address: _____

Creating the Financial Framework

Income
SUPPORT
Sponsors - Major Cash
Sponsors - Contributing Cash
In-Kind Contributions - Break Down by Committees
On-Site Donations

REVENUE
MARKETING
Online Tickets - list each ticket type's total revenue as a separate line item including comp tickets
Online Donations

MERCHANDISE
Online Merchandise* - list each item's total revenue as a separate line item
On-Site Merchandise* - list each item's total revenue as a separate line item
Inventory - unsold inventory is an asset
*Note: List each size separately with total revenue to establish purchasing history.

SITE SERVICES
Concessions/Vendors Flat Fees or Percentage of Gross Sales
Beverage Sales
Ice Sales
Promotional Banners, Tablecloths, etc.
Sales Tax on Beverage and Ice Sales

OTHER
Interest Income

Expenses
SPONSOR SERVICES
Sponsor Administrative - mailings, postage, invitations, copies, nametags, etc.
Sponsor Posters - as per sponsorship agreement
Poster Framing - as per sponsorship agreement
Sponsor Reception - food and drink
Sponsor Tee Shirts - as per sponsorship agreement
Plaques - sponsors, special recognition
Photography/Video - photos included with sponsor thank-you letters and notes and inserted into next year's sponsorship presentations; B-roll video
Major and Contributing Sponsor Banner - created by the event and hung above the main stage
Rental - Sponsor VIP Hospitality Tent, string lights, tables, chairs, etc. and VIP seating
Miscellaneous - cups, napkins, etc.

MARKETING SERVICES
Marketing Administrative - mailings, postage, copies, etc.
Brand Identity Package - logo, stationery, creative design, website design
Website - domain name, hosting, secure certificates, content management online subscription service, custom programming, eCommerce plug-ins, etc.

Stock Photography - online subscription service
Photography/Video - shoots, editing
Email Marketing - online subscription service
Collateral - brochures, programs, schedules, fliers, etc.
Trademark and Copyright - fees and renewals
Online Tickets - credit card charge fees, percentage rate and ticket fees
Online Donations - credit card charge fees, percentage rate and ticket fees
Other Fees
Advertising - pre- and post-event

PUBLIC RELATIONS AND PUBLICITY
Public Relations and Publicity Administrative - mailings, postage, copies, etc.
News Releases - news distribution service, postage, envelopes, letterhead, etc.

MERCHANDISE
Merchandise Administrative - mailings, postage, copies, etc.
Poster - honorarium to artist, creative design, production, props, printing, etc.
Inventory Control - labels, scanners, stickers, plastic bags, heat sealer
Online Merchandise* - credit card charge fees, percentage rate and service fees
Shipping - boxes, tubes, mailers, postage, ground service for merchandise pre- and post-event
Handling - if outsourced
Storage Trailer Rental - for inventory control during the event
Merchandise Booth - decorations, string lights, tables, chairs, etc.
On-Site Phone - to process credit card transactions
On-Site Merchandise* - credit card charge fees, percentage rate and service fees
Sales Tax - retail merchandise
Promotional Banners - similar to other concessionaires
Miscellaneous
*Note: List each size separately to establish ordering history. Online and on-site credit card requirements differ.

SITE SERVICES
Site Administrative - mailings, postage, copies, etc.
Equipment Rental - tents, string lights, tables, chairs, etc.
Fencing and Barricades
Portable Toilets
Security Vendor - overnight patrol
Security Administrative - nametags, VIP credentials and parking passes, copies, etc.
Insurance
Licenses and Permits
Refrigeration Truck Rental
Beverages - product, containers, ice scoops
Ice - ice and trolley/cart
Sales Tax - beverages and ice
Resale Items - promotional banners, tablecloths, etc.
Event Signs - traffic, directional, informational, insurance requirements
Contract Labor - to assist with load in and load out of heavy equipment from storage facility
Radio Communications - used by Organizing Committee during the event
Miscellaneous - trash bags, trash boxes, etc.

ENTERTAINMENT
Entertainment Administrative - mailings, postage, copies, etc.
Talent - headliners, artists, speakers, musicians, pilots, performers, wine makers, authors, chefs, entertainers, brewmasters, etc.
Air Transportation - tickets, oversized baggage, equipment, samples, etc.
Ground Transportation - car rental, gas, insurance, car wash
Licenses - ASCAP, BMI
Sound Equipment and Technical Services
Lighting Equipment and Technical Services
Equipment Rental Specific to Acts - risers, pianos, stove, sink, portable kitchen, drum set, etc.
Contract Labor - to assist with load in and load out of heavy equipment from storage facility
Merchandise - gifts to entertainers - list each item's total cost as a separate line item
Merchandise - gifts to stage crew - list each item's total cost as a separate line item
Equipment Rental General - Talent Hospitality Tent/Green Room, string lights, tables, chairs, etc.
Contract Requirements - recreational vehicle (RV)/Green Room, food and beverages, etc.
Stage Crew - coolers, food and beverages, ice, etc.
Miscellaneous - duct tape, large rolls of plastic, broom, squeegee, etc.

VOLUNTEER SERVICES
Volunteer Administrative - mailings, postage, copies, etc.
Volunteer Sign-Up System - online subscription service
Equipment Rental - check-in/information booth tents, string lights, tables, chairs, etc.
Volunteer - nametags, credentials, passes, etc.
Thank You/Recognition - printing
Miscellaneous

TREASURER
Treasurer Administrative - mailings, postage, copies, etc.
Equipment Rental - trailer or on-site event office
Cash Registers, Drawers or Boxes
Credit Card Readers
Calculators
Cash Counting Machines
Bank Fees - checking account
Donation Jars - carpenter and designer services
Audit
Accounting Services - local and/or online subscription service
Income Tax Return - federal and state
Annual Corporate Filing Fee
Miscellaneous - adding machine tape, brown paper bags, receipt book, etc.

EVENT CHAIRMAN
Chairman Administrative - mailings, postage, copies, etc.
Poster Framing - gifts to community VIPs, elected officials, etc.
Merchandise - gifts to community VIPs - list each item's total cost as a separate line item
Legal Services - prepare and review contracts/agreements
Dues and Publications - destination management organizations (DMOs) - chamber of commerce, convention and visitors bureau or state tourism agency - dues, association membership dues, industry specific trade publication subscription fee
Gifts for the Organizing Committee

Photography - Organizing Committee and community VIPs
Miscellaneous - parking passes for community VIPs, baked goods for meeting with economic development agency, tee shirts for DMO travel agent familiarization (FAM) trip, pizza party for the Organizing Committee after hours during the event and wrap-up session food and beverages

SECRETARY or ADMINISTRATIVE ASSISTANT
Administrative - mailings, postage, copies, etc.
Stationery - letterhead, envelopes, etc.
File Boxes or Cabinet
Data/Cloud Storage - online subscription service
Telephone Service
Internet/Wi-Fi Service
Answering Machine (may be part of telephone service)
Office Space - if used during select months or year-round
Storage Space - materials and equipment

Voice Mail Recordings

PRE EVENT

Thank you for calling the [Event Name]. The event dates are [Day of the Week] to [Day of the Week, Month Date to Date].

For more information, please visit our website: [say the website domain name] www.eventdomainname.com [and then spell it out phonetically] or write to: [Event Name], [Mailing Address, City, State and Zip Code].

Or leave a brief message at the tone with your name, date and telephone number, including area code.

Our volunteers pick up messages at least once a week. Thank you for calling.

Note: Once talent - headliners, artists, speakers, musicians, pilots, performers, wine makers, authors, chefs, entertainers, brewmasters, etc. - is announced, add the event's schedule by day. Include directions and indicate information concerning alcohol, pets, coolers and concessions.

POST EVENT

Thank you for calling the [Event Name].

We hope you enjoyed the event and look forward to seeing you next year during the [generic time frame, for example, Memorial Day Weekend, first weekend in June, end of November].

Our volunteers check for messages at least once a week throughout the year so please leave your name, telephone number including area code and time of your call after the beep. Thank you.

For more information, please visit our website: [say the website domain name] www.eventdomainname.com [and then spell it out phonetically] or write to: [Event Name], [Mailing Address, City, State and Zip Code].

Model Release

I, the undersigned, hereby grant to [Full Legal Event Name] the absolute an irrevocable right and permission to use the photographs and/or videos taken of me or me in which I am included with others. Specifically:

1. To copyright the same in its own name or any other name that it may choose.

2. To use, re-use, publish and re-publish the same in whole or in part, individually or in conjunction with other photographs and/or videos, in any medium and for any purpose whatsoever, including but not limited to illustration, promotion, advertising, trade and Internet without restriction as to changes or alterations.

I hereby release and discharge [Full Legal Event Name] from any and all claims and demands arising out of or in connection with the use of the photographs and/or videos.

This authorization and release shall also extend to the benefit of anyone connected with [Full Legal Event Name], including legal representatives, licensees and assigns of [Full Legal Event Name] as well as the persons who took the photographs and/or videos.

I hereby warrant that I am of full legal age and have the right to sign my own name below. This release shall be binding upon me and my heirs, legal representatives, and assigns in perpetuity.

No promises have been made to me and no consideration is involved for this right or permission to use, or in securing my signature below other than the benefits to me by the taking and use of said photographs and name.

Signature: _____   Date: _____

Print full legal name: _____

Minor Model Release

I, the undersigned, hereby grant to [Full Legal Event Name] the absolute an irrevocable right and permission to use the photographs and/or videos taken of the minor named below or in which minor is included with others. Specifically:

1. To copyright the same in its own name or any other name that it may choose.

2. To use, re-use, publish and re-publish the same in whole or in part, individually or in conjunction with other photographs and/or videos, in any medium and for any purpose whatsoever, including but not limited to illustration, promotion, advertising, trade and Internet without restriction as to changes or alterations.

I hereby release and discharge [Full Legal Event Name] from any and all claims and demands arising out of or in connection with the use of the photographs and/or videos.

This authorization and release shall also extend to the benefit of anyone connected with [Full Legal Event Name], including legal representatives, licensees and assigns of [Full Legal Event Name] as well as the persons who took the photographs and/or videos.

I hereby warrant that I am of full legal age and have the right to sign my own name below for this minor in the above matter. This release shall be binding upon me and my heirs, legal representatives, and assigns in perpetuity.

No promises have been made to me or to the minor and no consideration is involved for this right or permission to use, or in securing my signature below other than the benefits to me by the taking and use of said photographs and name.

Signature: _____ Date: _____

Print full legal name: _____

Print minor's full legal name: _____

Survey 1

Xth Annual [Event Name]
Audience Survey

Date: *[or if your online system can collect a date and time, eliminate this information]*

1. I am a resident of City: _____ State: _____ Zip Code: _____

2. I am _____ years old

3. I am ☐ Male ☐ Female

4. I am attending the [Event Name] with _____ number of people

5. I plan to attend the [Event Name] on ☐ [X Day] ☐ [YDay] ☐ [XY Day] ☐ [XZ Day]

6. I have attended past [Event Names] in ☐ 20XS ☐ 20XT ☐ 20XU ☐ 20XV ☐ 20XW ☐ 20XX

7. I learned about the [Event Name] from: *(check all that apply)*

   ☐ Newspaper   Which one(s)? _____

   ☐ Television   Which station(s)? _____

   ☐ Radio   Which station(s)? _____

   ☐ Table Tent   What location? _____

   ☐ Poster/Flier   Where? _____

   ☐ Family/Friends

   ☐ Blog   Which one(s)? _____

   ☐ Event's website

   ☐ Other Website   Which one(s)? _____

   ☐ Social Media   Which one(s)? _____

   ☐ Destination Management Organization (CVB, Chamber of Commerce, Visitor Center)

            Which one(s)? _____

   ☐ Other   Please specify: _____

8. I plan to purchase the following items:

   ☐ Item from a prior year   ☐ Item from the current year

   ☐ Tee shirt   ☐ Poster   ☐ Hat   ☐ Coffee Mug

   ☐ Other items I would like to purchase: _____

9. Was the sound system ☐ Too loud? ☐ Not loud enough? ☐ Fine?

10. I plan to attend other [Event Names] in the future. ☐ Yes ☐ No

11. I would like to [see, hear, watch] at a future [Event Name]: _____

12. I/we would like to be added to your email list.

    I/we understand this list will not be sold, rented or given away for any purpose.
    Email: _____   Email: _____

    An email sign-up form is also available on the [Event Name] website: http://www.eventdomainname.com.

13. If you are vacationing, please answer the following questions:

    What city(s) are you visiting? _____
    Where are you staying?   ☐ With family   ☐ With friends   ☐ Hotel, motel, condo or campground
    How long are you staying in [County Name] County? _____
    Is this your first visit to [City Name]?   ☐ Yes   ☐ No
    Did you visit [City Name] specifically for the [Event Name]   ☐ Yes   ☐ No

14. General comments:

    _____
    _____
    _____

Survey 2

Xth Annual [Event Name]
Audience Survey

Your opinion is very important to the planners and sponsors of the [Event Name]. We would appreciate your taking a moment to complete this survey. Thank you!

1. Your Age:

   ☐ 18 and under   ☐ 19 to 25   ☐ 26 to 40   ☐ 41 to 55   ☐ 56 plus

2. How did you learn about [Event Name]? *(check all that apply)*

   ☐ Newspaper   ☐ TV   ☐ Radio   ☐ Word of Mouth   ☐ Other

3. Is this the first year you have attended the [Event Name]?   ☐ Yes   ☐ No

4. Which day(s) have you, or will you, attend the [Event Name]?

   ☐ [X1 Day]   ☐ [X2 Day]   ☐ [X3 Day]   ☐ [X4 Day]

5. What were your impressions of the 20XX [Event Name]?

   | Musical Performance | ☐ Excellent | ☐ Good | ☐ Average | ☐ Poor | ☐ Very Poor |

   Comments: _____

   | Sound System | ☐ Excellent | ☐ Good | ☐ Average | ☐ Poor | ☐ Very Poor |

   Comments: _____

   | Setting/Facilities | ☐ Excellent | ☐ Good | ☐ Average | ☐ Poor | ☐ Very Poor |

   Comments: _____

   | Food/Drink | ☐ Excellent | ☐ Good | ☐ Average | ☐ Poor | ☐ Very Poor |

   Comments: _____

   | Overall Impression | ☐ Excellent | ☐ Good | ☐ Average | ☐ Poor | ☐ Very Poor |

   Comments: _____

   | Parking | ☐ Excellent | ☐ Good | ☐ Average | ☐ Poor | ☐ Very Poor |

   Comments: _____

6. If you are a [State Name] Resident, please indicate the county where you live, and skip to question #8.

7. If you are not a [State Name] Resident, indicate where you live.

   City: _____   State: _____   Country: _____

Duration of Stay: ☐ Few Days   ☐ Week   ☐ Extended Visit

8. Reason for Visit: *(check all that apply)*

☐ Family/Friends   ☐ Beach   ☐ Attractions   ☐ Mountains   ☐ Business   ☐ [Event Name]

Accommodations:
☐ With Family   ☐ With Friends   ☐ Hotel/motel/condo   ☐ Other:_____

9. Yearly Household Income: *(optional)*

☐ Under $XX,XXX   ☐ $XX,XXX to $XX,XXX
☐ $XX,XXX to $XX,XXX   ☐ $XX,XXX to $XX,XXX

10. Do you have any suggestions to help make next year's [Event Name] better?

_____

11. Please identify as many [Event Name] sponsors as you can?

_____

12. Are you an employee of an [Event Name] sponsor?   ☐ Yes   ☐ No

13. Optional: ☐ I am interested in becoming a volunteer for the [Event Name].

Name: _____

Address: _____

City: _____   State: _____   Zip Code: _____

14. I/we would like to be added to your email list.

I/we understand this list will not be sold, rented or given away for any purpose.

Email: _____   Email: _____

An email sign-up form is also available on the [Event Name] website: http://www.eventdomainname.com.

Survey 3

Xth Annual [Event Name]
Audience Survey

Name: _____

Address: _____

City: _____ State: _____ Zip Code: _____

1. What is your gender?   ☐ Male   ☐ Female

2. Which best describes your visit to the area?

   ☐ Attend this specific event
   ☐ Vacation
   ☐ Visit with family or friends
   ☐ Business
   ☐ Other _____

3. What is your age?

   ☐ Under 20   ☐ 20-29   ☐ 30-39   ☐ 40-49   ☐ 50-59   ☐ 60 and over

4. How did you hear about the event? *(check all that apply)*

   ☐ Radio
   ☐ Newspaper
   ☐ TV
   ☐ Internet *(check all that apply)*
      ☐ Social media. Please list which ones: _____
      ☐ Blog
      ☐ Website
   ☐ Advertisement in a specific publication
   ☐ Other: _____

5. How do you feel about the [Event Name]? *(check all that apply)*

   ☐ Fine - I like it just the way it is
   ☐ Needs more [wine booths, beer vendors, entertainers, music, chef demonstrations]
   ☐ A different location is desired
   ☐ A different time of year is preferred
   ☐ Number of days - too many

☐ Number of days - not enough

☐ Parking - just right

☐ Parking - not enough

☐ Inbound traffic to the event - an issue?

☐ Outbound traffic to the event - an issue?

☐ Access to tickets should be limited to local businesses (*Ask only if tickets are available online or on site.*)

☐ Access to tickets should be available online (*Ask only if not using online tickets.*)

☐ Access to tickets should be available on site (*Ask only if tickets are only available in advance.*)

☐ Other: _____

6. I/we would like to be added to your email list.

    I/we understand this list will not be sold, rented or given away for any other purpose.

    Email: _____   Email: _____

    An email sign-up form is also available on the [Event Name] website: http://www.eventdomainname.com.

7. What best describes your place of residence?

    ☐ [Region Name] resident (within 20 miles)

    ☐ Visitor from within the state (outside 20 miles)

    ☐ Visitor from outside the state

8. Which best describes your stay during the event?

    ☐ Downtown hotel

    ☐ Hotel on the beach

    ☐ With family

    ☐ With friends

    ☐ Day visitor

    ☐ Other: _____

News Release Topics

Note: First-time events are not annual. They only become annual in the second year, unless an event is held every other year and then the event is held biennially. First time events are often described as inaugural events.

Below is a list of possible news release topics:

Mark Your Calendar for [Month Date or Date Range], 20XX
for the Xth Annual [Event Name]

Bob Jones Named Honorary Chairman of the Xth Annual [Event Name]

[Name] to Headline the Xth Annual [Event Name]

[Name] Brought Back by Popular Demand

Best Selling Author [Name] to Speak at the Xth Annual [Event Name]

Author of Book Title Announced as Keynote Speaker at the Xth Annual [Event Name]

Award-Winning Chef [Name] to Demonstrate How to XXXXX

Craft Beer Competition to Feature X, Y and Z

Award-Winning Wine Makers to be Showcased at Xth Annual [Event Name]

Bonded Wineries in XYZ Region Invited to Enter Wine Competition

BBQ Champs Return to Compete for Title

Design Contest Announced for Xth Annual [Event Name] Poster

[Name], [Name] and [Name] to Judge Wines at the Xth Annual [Event Name]

Downtown Kick-Off Party Slated for [Day of the Week, Month Date]

[Name] to Headline [Day of the Week] Night at the Xth Annual [Event Name]

Complete Line-up Announced for the Xth Annual [Event Name]

Music Lovers Mark Your Calendar for Xth Annual [Event Name]

Xth Annual [Event Name] Poster Unveiled

XYZ Event Tickets Now On Sale

Discount Tickets Now on Sale Until [Day of the Week, Month Date]

Tickets for the Xth Annual [Event Name] Now on Sale Online

Call for Volunteers for Xth Annual [Event Name]

Xth Annual [Event Name] Is Free Thanks to Sponsors

Children's Activities Added to [Event Name] Line-Up

Proceeds from the Xth Annual [Event Name] to Benefit Scholarships

[Event Name] Sizzles with Saucy and Spicy Food

[Event Name] Mixes Great Food with [Style of Music]

After Hours Jam Sessions Announced

Scholarship Winners Announced

Related Events to Round Out Xth Annual [Event Name]

Wine Competition Medalists Announced for Xth Annual [Event Name]

Diners and Judges to Select Winners

Brewery Tours Added to Craft Beer Competition Schedule

Parking Readily Available for the Xth Annual [Event Name]
Note: Attach a map with the number of spaces listed for each parking lot, deck or garage.

Host Hotel Packages Now Available

A Perfect Combination - [Destination's Assets] with [Event Name]

Beer Festival Announces Musical Acts

Applications Now Available for Food Vendors and Exhibitors

Cooking Contest to Showcase Local Products

Social Media Objectives, Strategies and Helpful Hints

Objective:

- To consistently promote the event brand/image to social media users, for example on Twitter, among a host of other networks or platforms.

- To use social media to connect and engage in dialogue with those who already have experienced the event and to create a connection with potential event-goers, sponsors, concessions/vendors, etc.

- To utilize social media to communicate with market segments that do and do not use traditional media.

- To develop a mechanism/standard to provide feedback to patrons and potential customers.

- To share the gained perspective (market intelligence) with the Event Chairman and the Marketing Services Committee Chairman in order to develop new strategies or make adjustments.

- To increase brand awareness and social capital but not necessarily event revenue.

Strategy:

- To communicate in a casual, common sense manner that espouses the values of the event.

- To communicate using standard language as well as shortcut or common texting abbreviations but still using proper grammar and spelling.

- To establish ties with organizations/others having relationships with the event, for example, sponsors.

- To feature relevant images and videos that support the event's values or the values of its demographics.

- To quickly update friends, groups, members, fans, followers and those who want more information about the event or its activities.

- To utilize social media to potentially reach target customers during pre- and post-event hours, for example, traffic conditions.

- To address concerns and opportunities as they may arise.

- To promote the event's social media platforms in its marketing and publicity materials.

Helpful Hints: Legal, Security, Professionalism, Courtesy and Timeliness

- Understand the fundamentals of trademark registration, copyrighted materials, model and property releases and use appropriately when posting on social media. For example, do not take images or logos from other websites or other locations without written permission (in advance) of the owner. Establish a system for documenting and storing "permissions."

- Recognize that content added/uploaded to some social media networks or platforms becomes its property.

- Recognize that any and all comments are public and should not include terms or thoughts that can be misinterpreted or taken the wrong way (if several interpretations).

- Understand the event's logos and images are trademarked and copyrighted, respectively, and should bear those designations, or credit or courtesy lines.

- Post signs in a conspicuous manner at all entry points stating photographing and videotaping will occur before, during and after the event. Clearly state that by being present at the event, event-goers give permission to being photographed and videotaped. Document the notices by taking a photo or video of the posted signs.

- In some situations, request permission from individuals being photographed. If the event plans to use the image in advertising and/or will see a financial gain by using the image/video, ask that a model release be signed. Then, file the release in the same system the event uses to store "permissions."

- Be careful with your personal information as well as that of the event. Not all information in your knowledge base is meant to be shared.

- Take care when it comes to potential security issues and use credible sources. Do not embed HTML coding into your social media pages unless provided by an approved/authorized person and do not click on links/ attachments from those that are unfamiliar.

- Avoid posting negative comments of your current and former sponsors, event chairmen, fellow volunteers, volunteer supervisor, concessions, etc.

- Recognize links to other websites serve as endorsements, for example, those running for office, promoting a business or products or services.

- Post to social media within the time frame approved by your volunteer supervisor. Timely posts are more valuable.

- Respond to immediate patrons' needs rather than responding to social media needs. Do not text in the presence of others unless approved to do so.

- Respond, but do not react, unless you have thoroughly thought through the response which may include discussion with a supervisor.

Public Service Announcement (PSA)

Xth Annual [Event Name]
[Month Date to Date, 20XX]
Suggested Public Service Announcement

The Xth Annual [Event Name] will swing into action from [Month Date to Date] with more than X hours of events from X [talent - headliners, artists, speakers, musicians, pilots, performers, wine makers, authors, chefs, entertainers, brewmasters, etc.]. The X-day event, presented by [Organizing Committee], will be held at [Venue/Location]. It's completely free to the public.

[Day of the Week] and [Day of the Week] hours are [X:XX a.m./p.m.] to [X:XX a.m./p.m.] and [Day of the Week] and [Day of the Week] hours are [X:XX a.m./p.m.] to [X:XX a.m./p.m.] Featured [talent - headliners, artists, speakers, musicians, pilots, performers, wine makers, authors, chefs, entertainers, brewmasters, etc.] are [Name], [Name], [Name], [Name] and [Name.]

For further information regarding the Xth Annual [Event Name], contact the [Organizing Committee] at www.eventdomainname.com.

PSAs - 10, 20 and 30 Second Radio Spots

Xth Annual [Event Name]
[Month Date to Date, 20XX]
(Suggested Public Service Announcements)

(10 seconds)
Don't miss this year's [in/out]door [Event Name], [Month Date to Date], in [descriptive word] [Venue/Location] in [location description] [City]. It's free.

Make plans now for this year's [in/out]door [Event Name], [Month Date to Date], in [location description] [City's] [descriptive word] [Venue/Location]. It's free.

Spend a [descriptive word] weekend at the [Event Name], [Month Date to Date], at [descriptive word] [Venue/Location] in [location description] [City]. It's free.

(20 seconds)
Enjoy X hours of [descriptive word] [event theme type] [in/out]doors at the [Event Name], [Month Date to Date]. X [event theme type] [talent - headliners, artists, speakers, musicians, pilots, performers, wine makers, authors, chefs, entertainers, brewmasters, etc.] at [descriptive word] [Venue/Location] in [location description] [City]. It's free.

Following the close of each [day's/night's] [Event Name], [Month Date to Date] at [X:XX a.m./p.m.], the [type of activity] goes on at the [Event Name's] [Related Event Name] where many of the [talent - headliners, artists, speakers, musicians, pilots, performers, wine makers, authors, chefs, entertainers, brewmasters, etc.] will come and [action word - sit, perform, cook, hang out] in the [Related Event Venue/Location] in [location description] [City]. It's free.

Plan a weekend of [descriptive word] [event theme type] at the free [in/out]door [Event Name], [Month Date to Date], overlooking the [view type] in [descriptive word] [Venue/Location]. It's free. Lots of great food and [event theme type], featuring [Name, Name and Name of select talent - headliners, artists, speakers, musicians, pilots, performers, wine makers, authors, chefs, entertainers, brewmasters, etc.]. Parking is plentiful.

(30 seconds)
If you're into [event theme type] -- make plans now for the Xth Annual [Event Name] with [in/out]door performances, [Month Date to Date] in [location description] [City's] [descriptive word] [Venue/Location], overlooking [view type]. What a spectacular setting for X hours of [descriptive word] [event theme type], featuring such international names as [Name, Name and Name of select talent - headliners, artists, speakers, musicians, pilots, performers, wine makers, authors, chefs, entertainers, brewmasters, etc.]. It's a complete weekend of [event theme type] with great food and plentiful parking wrapped up each night with the popular [Related Event Name] beginning at [X:XX a.m./p.m.] at the [Related Event Venue/Location] in [location description] [City]. Don't miss a single [performance/show/event] -- Admission is free! For more information, go to: www.eventdomainname.com or call XXX-XXX-XXXX.

Photo/Video Opportunities

Xth Annual [Event Name]
Photo/Video Opportunities*
at City-County Airport

Who: A six-person honor guard composed of members of fire, police and emergency medical service units (representing three branches of military service) will participate along with a team of parachuters.

What: The Really Really Big Air Show at City-County Airport will honor 9/11 rescue workers as part of a show of patriotism during the opening ceremony each day.

Tentatively, an Air Force C-17 is scheduled to do a "fly over" as part of the ceremony. A cargo aircraft, it is operated by the Air Mobility Command at the XXXth Airlift Wing, [Name] Air Force Base, and the XXth Airlift Wing (Associate Reserve), also at [Name] Air Force Base.

A team of parachuters descending on the airport with the final member, a flag jumper, displaying an American flag, will close the ceremony.

Where: City-County Airport, [Physical Address, City, State and Zip Code].
Located on the east side of U.S. Highway XX, north of Interstate XX.

When: [Day of the Week, Month Date] and [Day of the Week, Month Date] at [X:XX a.m./p.m.], only a few days before the 9/11 anniversary.

How: For more information in advance of the air show dates, contact:
[Name], Public Information Officer, City-County Airport at XXX-XXX-XXXX,
pio@city-co-airport.com or visit www.eventdomainname.com.

Note: On show days, the media are asked to enter at the main gate. Volunteers at the gate will direct you to the specific staging areas.

*Subject to weather conditions.

Media Day

Xth Annual [Event Name]
Media Day* at City-County Airport
An Aerial View

Who: Members of the local media.

What: The Really Really Big Air Show at City-County Airport invites members of the local media to see the City-County Airport and surrounding areas from a different perspective and to take aerial photos and B-roll footage. Flights, pending seat availability and weather conditions, can also include aerobatic maneuvers.

Advance notice requested.

Where: City-County Airport, [Physical Address, City, State and Zip Code].
Located on the east side of U.S. Highway XX, north of Interstate XX.

When: [Day of the Week, Month Date] at [X:XX a.m./p.m.]

How: For more information in advance of the air show dates, contact:
[Name], Public Information Officer, City-County Airport at XXX-XXX-XXXX, pio@city-co-airport.com or visit www.eventdomainname.com.

Note: On show days, the media are asked to enter at the main gate. Volunteers at the gate will direct you to the specific staging areas.

*Subject to weather conditions.

The Booking Process

One of the best ways to budget for talent is to build three matrices: 1) projected talent costs; 2) projected airfare costs and 3) projected room night stays. Realize if one talent level price goes up, another will need to come down. To make this work, bottom line expenses shouldn't increase. Here's an example of how these matrices works:

TALENT
Talent   Calculate an average rate within each category
Level A (Headliner)   4 nights @ $15,000 = $60,000
Level B (Opening Act)   4 nights @ $8,000 = $32,000
Level C (Late Afternoon)   4 days @ $5,000 = $20,000
Level D (National/State Act)   4 days @ $2,500 = $10,000
Level E (Regional/Local Act)   4 days @ $1,000 = $ 4,000

                                                                        $126,000

HOTEL ROOM NIGHT STAYS*
Level A (Headliner)   4 nights x 5 people in a group = 20 x 2 (nights each) = 40
Level B (Opening Act)   4 nights x 4 people in a group = 16 x 2 (nights each) = 32
Level C (Late Afternoon)   4 nights x 4 people in a group = 16 x 2 (nights each) = 32
Level D (National/State Act)   4 nights x 4 people in a group = 16 x 2 (nights each) = 32
Level E (Regional/Local Act)   NONE

*Note: Verify that the number of hotel room nights does not exceed the sponsor hotel's allocation   136 room nights
as per the hotel's contract and the sponsorship agreement.*

AIRFARES
Level A – Airfare between X and Y   4 different flights with 5 people per = 20 x $400 airfares = $8,000
Level B – Airfare between W and Y   4 different flights with 4 people per = 16 x $260 airfares = $4,160
Level C – Airfare between Z and Y   4 different flights with 8 people per = 32 x $120 airfares = $3,840

                                                                        42 airfares = $16,000

Letter of Intent

Date

[Contact Person and Title]
[Company Name]
[Mailing Address]
[City, State and Zip Code]

Dear [Name]:
Thank you for your interest in the Xth Annual [Event Name]. This year's exciting festival will take place [Month Date to Date, 20XX], in [Venue/Location] in [City, State].

It is our intent to feature you [Talent Name if a group or if being sent to a management firm] in our program for the amount of $XX,XXX plus airfare and hotel accommodations. Our plan for funding will be finalized in the near future [or by Month Date] at which time we will confirm our commitment to you.

[Option 1] We will be in touch shortly to reconfirm your or your group's availability and to request your contract and promotional materials.

[Option 2] We will be in touch shortly to reconfirm your or your group's availability and to send you a contract and request other pertinent promotional materials.

Thank you.

Sincerely,

[Name]
Entertainment Committee Chairman
entertainment@eventdomainname.com
XXX-XXX-XXXX

[Name]
Talent/Programming Coordinator
talent@eventdomainname.com
XXX-XXX-XXXX

Letter of Commitment

Date

[Contact Person and Title]
[Company Name]
[Mailing Address]
[City, State and Zip Code]

Dear [Name]:

The Xth Annual [Event Name] is pleased to include you [Talent Name if a group or if being sent to a management firm] in this year's program.

The exact time of your [or Talent Name's] performance is scheduled for [Day of the Week, Month Date, 20XX], [X:XX a.m./p.m. or yet to be determined]. The performance is scheduled in the [Venue/Location] in [City, State].

[Option 1a - Provided Contract with No Deposit] Please find enclosed a signed agreement with musician's fee to be paid as designated in the contract.

[Option 1b - Provided Contract with Event Addendum] We have received your contract. Please sign all three copies of the attached addendum and return to us by [Day of the Week, Month Date, 20XX]. We will then sign and return a fully executed contract to you, along with a deposit. A self-addressed envelope has been provided for your convenience.

[Option 1c - Provided Contract and with Returned Addendum] Please find enclosed a copy of the fully executed agreement.

[Option 1d - Provided Contract and with Returned Addendum and Deposit] Please find enclosed a copy of the fully executed agreement with deposit.

[Option 2a - Event Contract with or without an Addendum] Please sign all three copies of the enclosed contract and return to us. We will sign and return to you a fully executed agreement. Please return to us as quickly as possible. A self-addressed envelope has been provided for your convenience.

Option 2b - Event Contract and with No Deposit] Please find enclosed a copy of the fully executed agreement.

[Option 2c - Event Contract and with Deposit] Please find enclosed a copy of the fully executed agreement with deposit.

Please verify the exact name of the group as listed in the contract, as this is how the event will promote talent in its marketing materials and on its website.

Our Stage Manager [Name] will be in contact with you regarding staging, microphone and monitor plots. For your convenience, we have included a list of the equipment the event will provide.

If [you, individual members of talent's group or your client] would be available for media interviews, please let us know.

[Option 3a] For advance publicity purposes, please forward link(s) to the talent's website(s). The event's Public Relations and Publicity Committee will prepare a brief description of talent and provide it to the media along with

this link. Also, please provide us a high resolution (300 dpi) 4-color photo of yourself or your group at 7" at its widest side in .jpg format. We are unable to use website images or accept photos taken on a smartphone as they are not of the caliber needed. With these materials, we will be better able to promote your performance.

[Option 3b] Thank you for providing us with a link to your website. This will enable us to better promote your performance.

[Option 4a] Please provide us your email address. Among other uses, it will be used to forward your hotel confirmation. We regret we are unable to extend your stay.

[Option 4b] Please provide us your email address. Among other uses, it will be used to forward your hotel confirmation and airline tickets. We regret we are unable to extend your stay.

Should you have any questions, please contact us.

Sincerely,

[Name]   [Name]
Entertainment Committee Chairman   Talent/Programming Coordinator
entertainment@eventdomainname.com   talent@eventdomainname.com
XXX-XXX-XXXX   XXX-XXX-XXXX

Basic Talent Agreement

[Full Legal Event Name]
Xth Annual [Event Name]
Talent Agreement

This Agreement is made and effective this [XX] day of [Month 20XX], by and between [Full Legal Event Name], a [State] [non-profit or for profit] corporation with its principal place of business located at [Physical and/or Mailing Address, City, State and Zip Code], herein after referred to as Event and [Legal Talent Name], hereinafter referred to as Talent.

In consideration of the mutual promises and undertakings of each of the parties hereto, and for other good and valuable consideration, the receipt and sufficiency of which is hereby acknowledged, the parties hereby agree as follows:

1. Event hereby agrees to employ Talent and Talent hereby accepts the engagement upon the following terms and conditions:

    a) [Event Name], [Venue/Location], [Physical Address, City, State and Zip Code];

    b) [Day of the Week, Month Date, 20XX] and [X:XX a.m./p.m.] to [X:XX a.m./p.m.] (All times referred to in this paragraph are [list specific time zone and indicate if during the event it will be part of Daylight Savings Time, or not.];

    c) Name of group: _____;

    d) Number of individuals in group: _____;

    e) Compensation to be paid by check to Talent: i) deposit of $XXX to be received by Talent no later than [Month Date, 20XX] and made payable to the order of: [Talent's, Agent's or Manager's Name].; and ii) balance of $XXX to be paid by check and made payable to the order of: [Talent's Name] or in cash upon completion of performance.

2. In the event of any dispute between the parties hereto arising out of this contract, the prevailing party shall be entitled to recover all attorney fees and costs incurred, in addition to any other damages or other recovery awarded by the Court.

3. Talent hereby agrees in the event the performance of Talent is canceled for any reason which is beyond the reasonable control of the Event, and not the fault of Talent, including, but not limited to, inclement weather, civil unrest, flood, hurricane, bomb threats or other reasons, any and all deposits, retainers or fees which have been paid in advance to Talent will be retained by Talent as liquidated damages and in full settlement of any claim which Talent may have had against the Event for the balance of its fee had Talent performed.

4. Talent will at all times conduct itself in an orderly manner during its performance and at all times while on the premises. In addition, Talent will abide by all rules and regulations which may be established by the Event.

5. Talent will use its best efforts to achieve the best possible performance.

6. If Talent is incapacitated from rendering services through sickness or otherwise, or, if Talent fails to perform except as specified in paragraph 3 of this Agreement, then all amounts which have been received by Talent in advance from the Event will be promptly refunded; however, this shall not preclude the Event from pursuing additional recourse against Talent for default.

7. Talent's scheduled time for its performance is subject to change by the Event, provided: a) Any change of the actual Agreement upon date of performance must be made in writing by the Event no later than two weeks before the performance and must be mutually agreed upon by both parties hereto to this Agreement. In any case, the dates must be limited to the dates of the Event, [Month Date to Date, 20XX] and b) Any change in the time of the performance on the agreed upon day shall be communicated to Talent in a timely fashion by the Event in order that both parties hereto may present the best possible performance.

8. Event agrees to provide equipment requested by Talent for the performance. Talent agrees equipment requested will not be unusual or excessive and a list of [specific equipment] will be sent to the Event no later than X weeks prior to the date of performance.

9. Event will be entitled to use Talent's name and/or photograph in advertisements or other publicity.

10. Talent shall be responsible to pay for any commissions which may be due to any agents or other parties and to indemnify the Event against all costs and expenses arising out of any such claims.

IN WITNESS WHEREOF, the parties have executed this Agreement the date and year first written above.

The attached Addendum A is a true and complete list of all Talent who are members of the group which is a party to this Agreement. However, Talent reserves the right to change personnel if, in his or her opinion, it is necessary to do so to insure the best possible performance. Their signatures hereon constitute their Agreement to be jointly and severally bound by the terms of this Agreement.

_____   _____
Witnesses   Talent Signature

_____   _____
Witnesses   Print Name

                                                   _____
                                                   Mailing Address

                                                   _____
                                                   City, State and Zip Code

                                                   [Full Legal Event Name]

                                                   By: _____
                                                   Signature

                                                   _____
                                                   Authorized Representative Title

Addendum A - Talent Agreement

The following is a true and complete list of Talent who are members of the group, which is the Talent referred to in this Agreement, and his/her/their signatures hereon constitute his/her/their Agreement to be jointly and severally bound by the terms of this Agreement.

_____	_____
Talent Signature	Talent Signature
_____	_____
Print Name	Print Name
_____	_____
Mailing Address	Mailing Address
_____	_____
City, State and Zip Code	City, State and Zip Code
_____	_____
Telephone	Telephone
_____	_____
Email	Email
_____	_____
Social Security Number	Social Security Number
_____	_____
Talent Signature	Talent Signature
_____	_____
Print Name	Print Name
_____	_____
Mailing Address	Mailing Address
_____	_____
City, State and Zip Code	City, State and Zip Code
_____	_____
Telephone	Telephone
_____	_____
Email	Email
_____	_____
Social Security Number	Social Security Number

_____

Talent Signature

_____

Print Name

_____

Mailing Address

_____

City, State and Zip Code

_____

Telephone

_____

Email

_____

Social Security Number

_____

Talent Signature

_____

Print Name

_____

Mailing Address

_____

City, State and Zip Code

_____

Telephone

_____

Email

_____

Social Security Number

_____

Talent Signature

_____

Print Name

_____

Mailing Address

_____

City, State and Zip Code

_____

Telephone

_____

Email

_____

Social Security Number

_____

Talent Signature

_____

Print Name

_____

Mailing Address

_____

City, State and Zip Code

_____

Telephone

_____

Email

_____

Social Security Number

Detailed Talent Contract

[Full Legal Event Name]
Xth Annual [Event Name]
Talent Contract

This contract is for the personal services of [Legal Talent Name (individual or group) or Talent's Agency or Management Firm] on the engagement described below and is made this [Day of the Week, Month Date 20XX], by and between the undersigned purchaser of Talent, [Full Legal Event Name], hereinafter called [Event Name] and the undersigned [Legal Talent Name (individual or group) or Talent's Agency or Management Firm], hereinafter referred to as Talent. Talent's services are being hereby retained for the [20XX] [Event Name] scheduled [Month Date to Date, 20XX], inclusive.

In consideration of the mutual promises and undertakings of each of the parties hereto and for other good and valuable consideration, the receipt and sufficiency of which are hereby acknowledged, [Event Name] hereby agrees to hire the services of Talent and Talent hereby agrees to provide its services to [Event Name], in accordance with the following terms and conditions:

1. Name of Talent: _____

   Lead Talent (whose personal services are essential hereunder): _____

   Number of individuals in group: _____

2. Location of Concert: [Venue/Location], [Physical Address, City, State]

3. Single engagement date: _____ from time: _____ p.m. to: _____ p.m.; (All times referred to in this paragraph are [list specific time zone and indicate if during the event it will be part of Daylight Savings Time, or not.]

4. Total Compensation Agreed Upon: _____
   a) deposit of $_____ to be received by Talent no later than [Month Date, 20XX] and made payable to the order of: [Talent's, Agent's or Manager's Name];

   b) balance of $_____ to be paid by check and made payable to the order of: [Talent's Name] or in cash upon completion of performance;

   c) _____X_____ room(s) for Y night(s) in a standard hotel room to be arranged by and provided by [Event Name]. This is based on single or double occupancy; and

   d)_____X_____ (one-way or round-trip) domestic coach airfares arranged by and provided by [Event Name].

5. Duties of Talent: To perform to the best of his/her/their abilities at [Event Name] on the date and time set for in paragraph 3 above.

6. Talent agrees in the event the performance of Talent is canceled for any reason which is beyond the reasonable control of [Event Name] and not the fault of the Talent, including, but not limited to, inclement weather, civil unrest, flood, hurricane, bomb threats, or other reasons, any and all deposits, retainers, or fees, which have been paid in advance to Talent will be retained by Talent as liquidated damages and in full settlement of any claim which Talent may have against [Event Name] for the balance of its fee had Talent performed hereunder.

7. Talent will at all times conduct himself/herself/themselves in an orderly manner during his/her/their performances and at all times while on the premises. In addition, Talent agrees to abide by all rules and regulations which may be established by the [Event Name] and currently established by local, state and federal governments.

8. Talent will use his/her/their best efforts to achieve the best possible performance. Talent also agrees to provide [Event Name] with stage, specific equipment needed, photographs and biographies and any other reasonably requested information at least thirty (30) days prior to the Talent's performance (approximately [Month Date, 20XX]). Unless hereinafter otherwise provided Talent shall provide all [instruments, tools, equipment, supporting materials, fuel, etc.] used by it in the delivery of its service hereunder at its own cost and expense.

9. If the Lead Talent of Talent, as identified in paragraph 1 above, is incapacitated from rendering services through sickness, injury, accident, refusal to work or otherwise, or if Talent fails to perform, then Talent shall immediately refund to [Event Name] all deposits which have been received by Talent in advance from the [Event Name]; however, this shall not preclude [Event Name] from pursuing additional recourse against Talent for default under this Agreement. If at any time during the engagement period referred to in paragraph 3 above, any member of Talent, except for the Lead Talent identified in paragraph 1 above, should become incapacitated and be unable to render his or her services, Talent shall immediately replace such member with competent Talent. The replacement shall have the same general abilities as the incapacitated member so that at all times during the engagement scheduled hereunder Talent shall have its full complement of personnel/talent.

10. Talent acknowledges Talent's scheduled time for its performance hereunder is subject to change by the [Event Name]; however, [Event Name] shall make every reasonable attempt to notify Talent of such change as much in advance thereof as is reasonably possible.

11. Talent hereby authorizes the use of Talent's name, signature and likeness, and biographical materials concerning Talent including, but not limited to, photographs of Talent by [Event Name] in advertisements and other publicity for the [Event Name].

12. Talent shall be responsible for paying any commissions which may be due to any agents or other parties, and hereby agrees to indemnify and hold [Event Name] harmless, from and against any and all losses, costs, liabilities, claims, demands and expenses whatsoever arising out of any such claims, including all attorney fees and costs therewith incurred before or during the trial period, and for all attorney fees and associated costs incurred on any appeal or appeals resulting therefrom.

13. A copy of the Management Agreement between Talent and his/her/their Agent must be attached if Agent is executing this contract for Talent. [Event Name] hereby reserves the right to reject this contract if [Event Name] is not provided such copy of the Management Agreement or if the Management Agreement does not meet the Talent's approval.

14. Talent represents and warrants it is under no disability, restrictions, or prohibition, whether contractual or otherwise, with respect to its rights to execute this Agreement and perform its terms and conditions, and with respect to its rights to perform at the Event, as set forth in paragraph 1 through 4 above. Talent shall indemnify and hold [Event Name] harmless from any loss or damage, including attorneys' fees, arising out of or connected with any claim by a third party which is inconsistent with any of the warranties or representations made by Talent in this Agreement. Talent shall reimburse [Event Name], on demand, for any payment made by [Event Name] at any time after the date hereof with respect to any liability or claim to which the foregoing indemnity applies. [Event Name] shall give Talent immediate notice of all such claims by a third party or all suits or actions brought against [Event Name] from such claims. Talent shall have the

right to participate fully within the settlement of such claims or the defense of such suits and actions.

15. Talent agrees to return this executed Agreement two (2) weeks from date of Talent's receipt of same (approximately [Month Date, 20XX]) to the [Event Name] at its principal place of business located at [Mailing Address, City, State and Zip Code].

16. Talent agrees any rider attached to this Agreement is an integral part of this Contract, is incorporated herein by reference, and Talent shall be equally bound thereby.

17. In the event of any dispute between the parties hereto arising out of this Agreement, the prevailing party in any litigation resulting therefrom shall be entitled to recover from the other party all its attorney fees and costs incurred, in addition to any other damages or other recovery awarded by the Court.

18. This Agreement contains the entire Agreement between [Event Name] and Talent with respect to the subject matter contained herein. No modification, amendment, waiver, termination, or discharge of the Agreement or of any provision thereof shall be binding upon the parties hereto unless confirmed by a written instrument signed by both [Event Name] and Talent. No waiver of any provision of this Agreement or any default hereunder shall affect [Event Name's] subsequent rights to enforce such provision or to exercise any rights or remedy in the event of any other default, whether or not similar.

19. This Agreement shall be deemed to have been made in the State of [State Name], and its validity, construction, and effect shall be governed by the laws of said State.

20. This Agreement is not assignable by Talent to any other party. [Event Name] can, however, assign its rights and obligations hereunder to any successor entity with a similar purpose and objective as that of [Event Name].

21. All notices of other documents to be delivered under this Agreement shall be in writing and delivered personally or mailed by regular mail, postage prepaid, addressed to the other party at the following address:

    a) IF TO [Event Name]:   [EVENT NAME]
                                     [MAILING ADDRESS]
                                     [CITY, STATE AND ZIP CODE] and

    b) IF TO Talent: [LEGAL TALENT NAME]
                                     [MAILING ADDRESS]
                                     [CITY, STATE AND ZIP CODE]

22. No delay or failure by either party to exercise any right under this Agreement, and no partial or single exercise of that right, shall constitute a waiver of that or any other right, unless otherwise expressly provided herein.

23. This Agreement shall be executed in two or more counterparts, each of which shall be deemed an original but all of which together shall constitute one and the same instrument.

24. The terms and provisions of this agreement shall be binding upon and inure to the benefits of each of the parties hereto and his/her/their respective successors and assigns.

IN WITNESS WHEREOF, the parties have executed this Contract the date and year first above written.

The attached Addendum A is a true and complete list of all Talent who are members of the group which is a party to this Agreement. However, Talent reserves the right to change personnel if, in his or her opinion, it is necessary to do so to insure the best possible performance. Their signatures hereon constitute their Agreement to be jointly and severally bound by the terms of this Agreement.

_____	_____
Witnesses	Agent or Manager
_____	_____
Witnesses	Talent Signature
	_____
	Print Name
	_____
	Mailing Address
	_____
	City, State and Zip Code

[Full Legal Event Name]

By: _____
Signature

_____
Authorized Representative Title

Note: The Main Event - Basic Talent Agreement - Addendum A can be copied and included as part of the Detailed Talent Contract.

Entertainment Master List

These three pages (Part 1, 2 and 3) can be combined into a single database file:

Part 1- Revision Date

	Stage Start Time	Commitment Letter Sent	Contract Sent	Contract to be Sent	Contract Returned	Fully Executed	PR Info Received
____day, Month Date							
Talent Group 1	6:00 p.m.	X	X		X	X	X
Talent Group 2	7:00 p.m.		X		X		X
Talent Group 3	8:00 p.m.		X			X	
Talent Group 4	9:00 p.m.		X				
____day, Month Date							
Talent Group 1	6:00 p.m.	X	X		X		
Talent Group 2	7:00 p.m.		X		X	X	X
Talent Group 3	8:00 p.m.		X		X	X	
Talent Group 4	9:00 p.m.		X		X		X
____day, Month Date							
Talent Group 1	1:00 p.m.		X				
Talent Group 2	2:00 p.m.		X		X		
Talent Group 3	3:00 p.m.		X				
Talent Group 4	4:00 p.m.		X				
Talent Group 5	5:00 p.m.	X					
Talent Group 6	6:00 p.m.	X					
Talent Group 7	7:00 p.m.	X	From Talent		X	X	X
Talent Group 8	8:00 p.m.	X		X			
Talent Group 9	9:00 p.m.	X		X			
Talent Group 10	10:00 p.m.	X					X
____day, Month Date							
Talent Group 1	1:00 p.m.		X				
Talent Group 2	2:00 p.m.		X		X	X	X
Talent Group 3	3:00 p.m.		X				
Talent Group 4	4:00 p.m.		X				
Talent Group 5	5:00 p.m.	X					
Talent Group 6	6:00 p.m.	X					
Talent Group 7	7:00 p.m.	X		From Talent			
Talent Group 8	8:00 p.m.	X					
Talent Group 9	9:00 p.m.	X					

Part 2

	Stage Layout Received	Equipment Needs*	No. in Group	Airfare Cities*	Set-up Day	Event Day 1	Event Day 2	Event Day 3	Event Day 4	Tear-Down Day
_____day, Month Date										
1	Yes	Standard	4	No		X				
2	Yes	Standard	5	No		X				
3	No	Electric Piano	5	No		X				
4	No	Standard	4	4-NYC-XYZ-NYC	X	X	X			
_____day, Month Date										
1	Yes	Standard	4	No			X			
2	Yes	Standard	4	No			X			
3	Yes	Standard	5	5-MIA-XYZ-NYC		X	X	X		
4	Yes	4 Mics	4	4-CHI-XYZ-CHI		X	X	X		
_____day, Month Date										
1	Yes	Standard	20	No				X		
2	Yes	Standard	6	No				X		
3	No	Standard	4	No				X		
4	No	Standard	5	1-SFO-XYZ-SFO			4X	X	X	
5	No	Standard	5	No				X		
6	No	Electric keyboard	4	4-NYC-XYZ-NYC			X	X	X	
7	No	Riser	4 + mgr	No (bus)				X	X	
8	No	Baby Grand	6	6-LAX-XYZ-LAX			X	X	X	
9	No	Baby Grand	5	5-NYC-XYZ-NYC			X	X	X	
10	No	Standard	8	No (bus)				X	X	
_____day, Month Date										
1	No	Standard	10	No					X	
2	Yes	Standard	4	No					X	
3	No	Baby Grand	5	No					X	
4	No	With Technician	5	No					X	
5	No	Standard	4	4-ATL-XYZ-ATL				X	X	X
6	Yes	Keyboard	5	5-NYC-XYZ-NYC					X	X
7	No	Percussion	5	5-DC-XYZ-DC				X	X	X
8	No.	Chairs for all	6	6-MSY-XYZ-MSY				X	X	X
9	No	Standard	4	No					X	
TOTALS			151	49 Airfares						

Note: The Equipment Needs column lists those items communicated to the person making travel arrangements and should be shared with the Stage Manager. The Airfare Cities column lists the three letter airport codes for the departing city, the airport used by the event and the final destination of talent. The number preceding the airport codes is the number of talent flying that route. Event Days columns indicate the dates talent are in the event city. Numbers indicate how many in the group have arrived when not the entire group.

Part 3

	Hotel Rooms Needed	Set-Up Day	Event Day 1	Event Day 2	Event Day 3	Event Day 4	Tear-Down Day	Deposit Required	Paid	Amount Due	Type	Total
	____day, Month Date											
1	No							--		$600.	Check	$600.
2	No							$500.	9/5	$2,000.	Check	$2,500.
3	No							--		-0-	--	-0-
4	Yes	4	4	4				$1,500.	10/1	$1,500.	Cash	$3,000.
	____day, Month Date											
1	No							--		$3,500.	Cash	$3,500.
2	No							--		$750.	Cash	$750.
3	Yes - 2 sharing		4	4	4			--	9/1	$650.	Check	$650.
4	Yes		4	4	4			$500.	9/1	$3,000.	Cash	$3,000.
	____day, Month Date											
1	No							--		$475.	Check	$475.
2	No							--		$550.	Check	$550.
3	No							--		$450.	Check	$450.
4	Yes - early arrival Day 2		4	5	5			--		5@$200.	Check	$1,000.
5	No							---		$450.	Check	$450.
6	Yes			4	4	4		$1,750.		$1,750.	Check	$3,500.
7	Yes - need bus parking			5	5			--		$2,000.	Cash	$2,000.
8	Yes - early arrival Day 2			6	6			--		$2,500.	Cash	$2,500.
9	Yes			5	5	5		$3,000.		$2,750.	Cash	$5,750.
10	Yes - need bus parking	8	8	8				$5,000.		$5,000.	Cash	$10,000.
	____day, Month Date											
1	No							--		$425.	Check	$425.
2								--		$475.	Check	$475.
3	No							--		$500.	Check	$500.
4	No							--		$1,000.	Cash	$1,000.
5	Yes				4	4	4	$600.	9/1	$1,500.	Cash	$2,100.
6	Yes					5	5	$500.	9/1	$4,500.	Cash	$5,000.
7	Yes				5	5	5	$3,000.	9/1	$3,000.	Cash	$6,000.
8	Yes.					6	6	$500.	9/1	$2,300.	Cash	$2,800.
9	No							--		$2,500.	Cash	$2,500.
	Sound and Lighting Crew											
--	Yes	4	4	4	4							
	TOTALS = 194 Room Nights	8	10	43	60	53	20	$16,850.		$44,525.		$61,375.
											Deposits	$16,850.
											Cash	$50,400.
											Checks	$10,975.

Airline Confirmation Letter

Date

[Contact Person and Title]
[Company Name]
[Mailing Address]
[City, State and Zip Code]

Dear [Name]:

Following your conversation with [First and Last Name] of XYZ Airline or [Travel Agency Name], your airline tickets were booked online and sent to the email address you provided. If the tickets did not appear in your inbox, please check your spam filter or contact [First Name] at XXX-XXX-XXXX or email him or her at: name@xyzairline.com or name@travelagency.com.

A member of the Transportation Committee - a driver with vehicle of ample size to handle your luggage and any equipment you previously communicated to the Stage Manager you planned to bring - will be parked in the cell phone lot awaiting your phone call. Please call this number to advise you have arrived: XXX-XXX-XXXX. He or she will then meet you outside baggage claim to transport you to [City Name], which is an approximate X-minute drive.

Your souvenir [Event Name] tee shirt and individual credentials will be given to you by your driver enabling you access to the Talent Hospitality Tent/Green Room and the stage for your performance.

Reservations have been confirmed for you at our official host hotel, [Hotel Name], [Physical Address, City, State and Zip Code]. The phone number is XXX-XXX-XXXX. From check-in until one hour prior to your performance, you will have free time. Please meet at the time and location specified your Transportation Committee driver and you will be transported to the [Venue/Location].

Afterwards a Transportation Committee member will confirm with you the date and time you will be picked up at the hotel for your outbound flight.

If you have any questions about your travel arrangements, please call [First Name] above or call me at XXX-XXX-XXXX.

Sincerely,

[Name]
Entertainment Committee Chairman
entertainment@eventdomainname.com
XXX-XXX-XXXX

Enclosure: Event Schedule

Welcome Letter

Xth Annual [Event Name]
Welcome to [City]

We are excited to have you participate in the Xth Annual [Event Name].

To make your stay more enjoyable, we have included information on [City Name] and additional information about the [Event Name] in this packet.

The Talent Hospitality Tent/Green Room is located at the venue and is available for the exclusive use of the event's talent. See the attached map for the exact location.

For those who have flown in, your credentials have been or will be provided to you by a member of the Transportation Committee. We regret space limitations and security considerations prohibit us from providing credentials to anyone other than the contracted talent.

For those planning to drive to the event from the hotel, your individual credentials, parking passes, directions to the [Venue Name] and a map with the venue location are enclosed. A security officer will assist you in parking your vehicle once inside the gate. Please note: some roads will be closed during the event so GPS mapping features may not bring you to the proper entry location.

We recommend you use the services of our Transportation Committee to travel from the hotel to the venue and back. They will have access to a special route and gate allowing them to avoid traffic. Please call the Transportation Committee Chairman at XXX-XXX-XXXX to make arrangements at least 6 hours prior to your performance.

A telephone is available at the venue for emergencies. The number is XXX-XXX-XXXX.

Details are now being finalized for the [related event] to be held at [Venue/Location], [Street Address, City] from [Day of the Week] to [Day of the Week, Month Date to Date] from [X:XX a.m./p.m.] to [X:XX a.m./p.m.] We invite you to attend and participate, if you desire.

Thank you for making this the best [Event Name] ever!

Sincerely,

[Name]   [Name]   [Name]
Entertainment Committee Chairman   Talent/Programming Coordinator   Hospitality Coordinator
entertainment@eventdomainname.com   talent@eventdomainname.com   XXX-XXX-XXXX
XXX-XXX-XXXX   XXX-XXX-XXXX

Volunteer Sign-Up Form

Note: In the past these have been paper sign-up sheets. Nowadays, much of the volunteer coordination can be done online with a simple survey, registration or volunteer management system. Once the information is submitted, the volunteer receives a confirmation detailing his or her desired volunteer job and preferred shift. Assignments will be reviewed by the Volunteer Services Committee and are subject to change.

Xth Annual [Event Name]
[Month Date to Date, 20XX]
Volunteer Sign Up

Name: _____

Mailing Address: _____

City: _____ State: _____ Zip Code: _____

Email: _____ Reconfirm Email: _____

Best phone number:

☐ Home: _____ Call between: _____ a.m./p.m. and _____ a.m./p.m.

☐ Cell: _____ Call between: _____ a.m./p.m. and _____ a.m./p.m.

☐ Text me using my cell number (above)

☐ Work: _____ Call between: _____ a.m./p.m. and _____ a.m./p.m.

Please list in order of preference the areas you are interested in volunteering with 1 being your first choice:

_____ Sponsor Services

_____ Volunteers

_____ Center Stage

_____ Merchandise

_____ Site

_____ Parking

_____ Concessions

_____ Beverage Stands/Trailers

_____ Ice

_____ Security

_____ Floater

Please select the shifts you are interested in volunteering.

[Day of the Week, Month Date] Event set-up	☐ 8:00 a.m. to 1:00 p.m. ☐ 1:00 p.m. to 6:00 p.m.
[Day of the Week, Month Date]	☐ 8:00 a.m. to 1:00 p.m. ☐ 1:00 p.m. to 6:00 p.m. ☐ 6:00 p.m. to 11:00 p.m.
[Day of the Week, Month Date]	☐ 8:00 a.m. to 1:00 p.m. ☐ 1:00 p.m. to 6:00 p.m. ☐ 6:00 p.m. to 11:00 p.m.
[Day of the Week, Month Date]	☐ 8:00 a.m. to 12:00 p.m. ☐ 12:00 p.m. to 4:00 p.m. ☐ 4:00 p.m. to 7:00 p.m. ☐ 7:00 p.m. to 11:00 p.m.
[Day of the Week, Month Date]	☐ 8:00 a.m. to 12:00 p.m. ☐ 12:00 p.m. to 4:00 p.m. ☐ 4:00 p.m. to 7:00 p.m. ☐ 7:00 p.m. to 11:00 p.m.
[Day of the Week, Month Date] Event tear down	☐ 8:00 a.m. to 1:00 p.m. ☐ 1:00 p.m. to 6:00 p.m.

☐ I can work more than one shift.
☐ I can only work one shift.
☐ My company is an event sponsor.

Sound and Lighting Bid

Note: If the Stage Manager desires to receive bids for apples, oranges, bananas and pears, just ask sound and lighting companies to send a bid. These are much more difficult to compare, so it's best for the event to create a bid request or request for proposal (RFP) dictating the event's needs. Allow ample space for bidders to insert pricing.

Date

[Contact Person and Title]
[Company Name]
[Mailing Address]
[City, State and Zip Code]

Dear [Name]:

The Xth Annual [Event Name] is now accepting bids for this year's event scheduled for [Day of the Week] to [Day of the Week, Month Date to Date, 20XX] at [Venue/Location] in [City, State]. Deadline to respond is: [Day of the Week, Month Date, 20XX] by [X:XX a.m./p.m.] This will allow our Entertainment Committee time to review the bids and present them to the Event Chairman for final review and approval, providing bid requirements are met.

In order to meet our event's needs, please include the following in your bid:

1. $_____ Staging and Additional Staging with minimum dimensions X' x X' (total 1). See attached diagram of existing stage and details about the structure.

2. $_____ Sound Wings - minimum dimensions X' x X' (total 2).

3. $_____ An Outdoor Covering/Roof/Tent - minimum dimensions X' x X' (total 1).

4. $_____ Sound Systems - for the main stage sound tower and sound wings.

5. $_____ Delay stacks (facing a specific direction) (total 2).

6. $_____ Delay stacks (facing the concessions) (total 2).

7. $_____ Lighting to include (please list quantity next to each): a) lifts ___; b) trusses ___; c) racks ___; d) canisters___; e) gobo (total X); f) controllers ___; g) dimmers ___; h) follow spots ___; and i) follow spot operators ___

8. $_____ Equipment rental: a) X piece [Brand Name, Model] drum kit with hardware and cymbals (total X); b) [Brand Name and Model] guitar amp or similar (total X); c) [Brand Name and Model] bass amp or similar (total X); and d) [Brand Name and Model] electric piano with stand (total X).

$_____ Complete Package Bid

The event will provide the following: scaffolding, screw jacks, planks and cross braces to serve as the sound and lighting equipment tower.

Bids should be inclusive, incorporating all transportation and labor costs from load in - throughout the event - and load out. The event will be unable to provide labor.

Please bid for each item separately. Should you be able to provide a bid for all items, please list above.

[Event Name] reserves the right not accept any of the bids.

Please provide us a list of references of similar events/festivals you have served in the past, along with a contact person and current phone number.

Please direct your bids to:

       Stage Manager
       [Event Name]
       [Mailing Address]
       [City, State and Zip Code]

Should you have any questions, please contact me.

Thank you.

Sincerely,

[Name]
Stage Manager
stagemanager@eventdomainname.com
XXX-XXX-XXXX

Call for Entries

Xth Annual [Event Name]
Creative Design Call for Entries

All regional artists are invited to submit a two-dimensional design to be used as the design theme for this year's [Event Name]. The design must be adaptable to a poster, tee shirt, billboard, program, advertisement, etc.

The [Event Name] is an X-day event, held [Month Date to Date], at [descriptive word] [Venue/Location] in [location description] [City].

SPECIFICATIONS

Type:	Two-dimensional artwork and/or photography
Size:	20" x 24" vertical or horizontal
Colors:	2 to 4 colors
Required elements:	[Event Name] and [Month Date to Date, 20XX]
	Schedule of the activities and sponsor names and/or logos
Theme:	Artists are encouraged to use the [event theme type], representative elements of the local area, region or state
Fine Print:	One submission per artist. On the back of each submission include the name of the artist, his or her mailing address, phone number and email address.

JUDGING

The competition will be judged by an X-person panel composed of representatives of: [Event Name], [Arts Agency], [Print Vendor] and [Arts Community Member].

HONORARIUM

A $XXX honorarium will be awarded to the winning submission. The judges reserve the right not to choose a winner from any of the entries.

RECOGNITION

The winning artist's name will be printed on the poster and he or she will be invited to attend the [Event Name] sponsor breakfast to unveil the poster.

The selected artist will be featured in a news release announcing the winning design and promoted on social media.

The artist will be invited to attend the event and will be introduced and recognized from the main stage.

COPYRIGHTS AND ASSIGNMENTS

The winning artist will retain copyrights to the work and will agree to assign all reproduction rights to the [Full Legal Event Name].

The winning artist will provide to the event in a timely manner a final digital file of the artwork in the requested format.

DEADLINE

All entries must be received by [X:XX a.m./p.m.] [Day of the Week, Month Date, 20XX] at the [Arts Agency Name], [Physical Address, City, State and Zip Code]. Notification will be by U.S. mail or email, no later than [Day of the Week, Month Date, 20XX].

Submissions not accepted may be picked up at the [Arts Agency Name] though [Day of the Week, Month Date, 20XX]. After this date, remaining submissions will be destroyed.

This competition is a joint promotion of the [Arts Agency Name] and the [Event Name] Organizing Committee.

QUESTIONS
Please contact the [Arts Agency Name] at XXX-XXX-XXXX or email@artsagencyname.com.

Poster Printing Bid Request

Xth Annual [Event Name]
Request for Proposal (RFP)
Poster Printing

Event: Xth Annual [Event Name] scheduled from [Day of the Week] to [Day of the Week, Month Date to Date, 20XX].

Background: The commemorative poster is framed and given to the event's sponsors and elected officials and is also used for promotional purposes - media, tourism agencies, VIPs, etc. The poster is sold before and during the event and is an important revenue-generating item.

Deadline: Bids are required to be returned no later than [Day of the Week, Month Date, 20XX] at [X:XX a.m./p.m.] (This is approximately 5.5 months prior to the event).

Pricing for: XX" wide x XX" high.

Stock: XYZ Stock by XYZ Vendor; or please list recommended paper, its weight and a description on the bid.

Quantities: X,XXX, X,XXX+, X,XXX++

Printing: 4-color one side with white reverse type on a dark background with heavy ink coverage; full bleed.

Pricing options: Please provide add-on pricing for: 1) dull spot varnish, a specific area of the poster overprinted with a clear matt finish varnish to add emphasis to key elements; 2) dull flood varnish; or 3) a clear matt varnish added to the entire surface to help reduce fingerprints.

Art: Final approved artwork will be provided by the event as a high resolution PDF with a .jpg proof, or as specified by the printer.

Packaging: Finished products shall be shrink wrapped in sets of 200 each with a cardboard bottom.

Schedule: Within 10 days of receipt of high resolution PDF, finished project to be delivered (see below). Assumes press time is set, giving 24 hours notice and event representative is available at time of press check.

Note: If a deposit is required with the signed contract, please advise amount due or percentage of total order. Detail when balance of payment is due.

Other:

- Prior to releasing the artwork to the printer, printing representatives are asked to sign a Do Not Disclose/ Confidentiality Statement* on behalf of all employees involved in the production and delivery process.

- Any and all make readies will be destroyed immediately. If used in the printer's portfolio, they shall be visibly stamped "sample."

- Printer to retain artwork on file for three years in the event client desires to produce additional posters.

- Please contact the event prior to destroying the working files.

- The printer, as part of printing industry standards, owns its working materials.

- The printer, as part of printing industry standards, can manufacture +/- 10% of the requested quantity. The final invoice will reflect the overage or underage.

- Original artwork is copyrighted to the [Event Name].

Delivery: Please deliver finished products within the city to an inside location with no visible samples attached to the outside of the containers. The address will be provided on acceptance of the winning bid.

Questions: [Name]
                  Merchandise Committee Chairman
                  msde@eventdomainname.com
                  XXX-XXX-XXXX

Note: This is only done under special circumstances.

Tee Shirt and Sweatshirt Bid Request

Xth Annual [Event Name]
Request for Proposal (RFP)
Tee Shirts and Sweatshirts

Event: Xth Annual [Event Name] scheduled for [Day of the Week] to [Day of the Week, Month Date to Date, 20XX]

Background: Printing of the event's tee shirts and sweatshirts is a two-part process. A small portion of the finished products are needed in advance of the event and the balance of the products are needed for, and possibly, during the event. The winning bid will be given to a single vendor.

Deadline: Bids are required to be returned no later than [Day of the Week, Month Date, 20XX[at [X:XX a.m./p.m.] (This is approximately 5.5 months prior to the event).

Pricing for the following:

1. Tee shirts - premium quality 100% preshrunk cotton in XYZ color or vendor recommended popular colors; please provide samples upon request. Please list manufacturer and manufacturer's product number, colors and color numbers on the bid.

2. Sweatshirts - premium quality heavyweight 50% cotton/50% polyester blend in XYZ color or vendor recommended popular colors; please provide samples upon request. Please list manufacturer and manufacturer's product number, colors and color numbers on the bid.

   Please advise if your suppliers see any challenges in obtaining certain products, colors or sizes within the next six months.

Printing: 4-color silkscreen process.
                 Image area not to exceed XX" wide x XX high."
                 Printing front side only; except Option A below.
                 Artwork and product must be colorfast.

Art: Final approved artwork will be provided as an .eps file with all fonts outlined with a .jpg proof, or as specified by the vendor.

Packaging: Finished products shall be bagged in clear plastic with one dozen items in each bag.
                 Each bag shall contain the same size.
                 Bags shall be boxed to standard quantities in a single box, same size, with outside of box clearly marked as to contents within each box. Box sealed with tape.

Schedule: Within 14 days of receipt of artwork (or next set of scheduled deadline for later phases), merchandise will be delivered (see below).

Option A: Sponsor Event, Presales and Opening Day
Quantity: Minimum pre-event order for XXX tee shirts and XXX sweatshirts

Other: Approximately XXX shirts will also be printed on the back in 1 color. Sponsor logos/artworks will be provided to the vendor prior to the event as an editable .eps file with fonts outlined.

Delivery: Please deliver finished products within the city to an inside location with no visible samples attached to the outside of the containers. The address will be provided on acceptance of the winning bid.

Option B: On Call Printing

Background: A quantity of tee shirt and sweatshirt inventory will be ordered prior to the event for use during the event.

Specifics: Based on the consumer's response to the design, additional inventory may be ordered during the event. The vendor will be given 24-hour notice to print a specific quantity of product for the next day.

                 Unprinted tee shirt and sweatshirt inventory - unused quantities (boxed cases) - will need to be returned to the merchandise supplier for a credit post event.

                 Please advise of the number of quality products which can be printed each hour.

Note: If a deposit is required with the signed contract, please advise amount due or percentage of total order. Detail when balance of payment is due.

Other:

   •   Prior to releasing the artwork to the printer, vendor representatives are asked to sign a Do Not Disclose/Confidentiality Statement* on behalf of all employees involved in the production and delivery process.

   •   Any and all make readies will be destroyed immediately. If used in the vendor's portfolio, they shall be visibly stamped "sample."

   •   Printer to retain artwork on file for three years in the event client desires to produce additional tee shirts and sweatshirts. Please contact the event prior to destroying the working files.

   •   The vendor, as part of industry standards, owns its working materials.

   •   Original artwork is copyrighted to the [Event Name].

Delivery: Please deliver finished products within the city to the event [Venue/Location]. Delivery shall be made to the Inventory Control Coordinator's on-site trailer. The address will be provided on acceptance of the winning bid.

Questions: [Name]
                 Merchandise Committee Chairman
                 msde@eventdomainname.com
                 XXX-XXX-XXXX

*Note: This is only done under special circumstances.

Registration/Application Form

Xth Annual [Event Name]
[Month Date to Date, 20XX]
Concessionaire Application - Paper or Online

As part of this application process, please find enclosed the [Event Name] schedule and map as well as the Concession Agreement which includes the rules and regulations governing the event's concession area.

You will be asked to confirm you have thoroughly read the Concessionaire Agreement before paying your application fee of $X,XXX which reserves your 10' x 20' leased space under the concession tent; string lights; two (2), eight-foot long folding tables; and four (4) chairs. Please note: minimal security is provided during the event.

After being reviewed by the Concession Committee, you will be notified if your organization has or has not been accepted as a concessionaire. If you are not selected, your $X,XXX application fee will be returned to you within 5 business days.

Selection criteria is as follows:

1. Quality food product.

2. Food product as it relates to variety of all concession applicants.

3. If a new concessionaire - reference checks with other festivals or similar events on: a) quality, b) cleanliness, c) speed of service, d) adaptability to a special event, e) cooperation with volunteers or staff, f) ability to meet deadlines, and g) ability to follow instructions.

4. If a former concessionaire - the committee will review and verify file notes from previous years to determine if the concession/vendor adhered to previous Concessionaire Agreements.

5. Suggested prices.

6. Will products be distributed in recyclable containers and/or with recyclable utensils and napkins?

Only approved concessionaires will be permitted in the [Venue/Location] during the Xth Annual [Event Name] and no unauthorized literature or promotional materials can be distributed.

Because of the amount of planning required to make all aspects of the event run smoothly, a concession planning meeting will be scheduled with all participating concessionaires. Every possible question will be answered at that time, as key contacts from the city will be available to address electrical or power sources and limitations, health department requirements, water and sewer access, garbage collection, vehicle access before the event, parking and parking passes, concession area credentials, availability of event tee shirts for your workers/volunteers, etc.

The event is considering renting a refrigeration storage truck. Concessionaires would be allowed to store products at their own risk, based on space availability, if rented.

Our local [Do-Good Civic Association chapter] will be manning the event's bottled water and soda (soft drinks or pop) concessions. As the event requires ice for this concession, we have arranged to have ice on site throughout the event and will make it available to all concessions at cost. We understand the need will be greatest during peak event times; as such, you will sign for the ice upon receipt and pay for it in cash at the end of the event.

The Concessionaire requests commercial leased space as follows:

Number of 10' Wide x 20' Long Spaces: _____

Product* and Price List: _____

_____

_____

_____

_____

_____

Concessionaire Legal Name: _____

Restaurant/Organization Name: _____

Concessionaire Name (to appear in promotional materials): _____

Contact Name: _____

Physical Address: _____

City: _____ State: _____ Zip Code: _____

Mailing Address: _____

City: _____ State: _____ Zip Code: _____

Contact Number: _____ Email address: _____

Cell Phone: _____ OK to send Texts to Cell: ☐ Yes ☐ No

*Note: When planning your proposed menu, remember this is a "quick" turnaround event. Make sure the food you are planning to prepare can be fixed quickly and is easy to prepare. All final menu selections are subject to the approval of the local health department. You will not be allowed to serve any item that has not been first approved by the [Event Name] Concession Committee and the health department prior to the start of the event. There will be no exceptions.

Application Review Point System

Xth Annual [Event Name]
[Month Date to Date, 20XX]
Concessionaire Application Review Point System

The following Concession Committee Members reviewed this applicant:
_____ , _____ and _____

Type of Food Products and Pricing: _____

_____

_____

_____

Once the points are calculated, review those concessions offering similar products and see if the Concession Committee desires to duplicate popular items or provide a concessionaire exclusivity in that food category.

Comments: _____

	Poor 1 Point	Below Average 2	Above Average 3	Superior 4
Quality	_____	_____	_____	_____
Cleanliness	_____	_____	_____	_____
Speed of Service	_____	_____	_____	_____
Adaptability to a Special Event	_____	_____	_____	_____
Cooperation with Volunteers	_____	_____	_____	_____
Meets Deadlines	_____	_____	_____	_____
Follows Instructions	_____	_____	_____	_____
Use of Recycled Packaging	_____	_____	_____	_____
TOTAL SCORE = _____	_____	_____	_____	_____

Personal visit by: _____ and _____

Concessionaire Agreement

Xth Annual [Event Name]
[Month Date to Date, 20XX]
Concessionaire Agreement
Flat Fee with Deposit

This Agreement is made and effective this [XX] day of [Month 20XX], by and between [Event Full Legal Name], a [State] [non-profit or for profit] corporation with its principal place of business located at [Physical and/or Mailing Address, City, State and Zip Code], hereinafter referred to as Lessor, and [Concessionaire Legal Name], with its principal place of business at [Physical Address, City, State and Zip Code], hereinafter referred to as Concessionaire. ·

Whereas, the Lessor will be producing the Xth Annual [Event Name] to be held in [Venue/Location] on [Month Date to Date, 20XX].

Whereas, the Lessor will sponsor various events to be held in the [Venue/Location] in connection with the Xth Annual [Event Name]; and

Whereas, it is the desire of Lessor to make available to persons attending and participating in the [Event Name] the above named business operated and conducted by Concessionaire.

NOW THEREFORE, the parties hereto do agree as follows:

1. Period of License: This Concessionaire Agreement is valid from [Day of the Week, Month Date, 20XX] beginning at [X:XX a.m./p.m.] to [Day of the Week, Month Date, 20XX] and ending at [X:XX a.m./p.m.] Failure to abide by the following rules and regulations will result in the removal of any concession from [Venue/Location] and the nearby-related restricted areas. Concession areas must be staffed at all times from at least 30 minutes before the first event begins each day until 30 minutes after the last event ends each day for the duration of the multi-day event period of the Xth Annual [Event Name].

2. All parties hereto this Agreement shall comply with all laws and pertinent rules of the State of [State Name], all pertinent county and city ordinances, including the health department, as well as the rules and regulations of Xth Annual [Event Name]. Such laws, ordinances, rules and regulations are expressly made a part of this Agreement.

3. The leased commercial space rules and regulations are listed and no other arrangements, oral or written, except as provided for in this Agreement, are binding upon the parties hereto.

4. Food, beverages and merchandise are restricted to only the sale of the agreed-upon items stipulated in this Agreement. No changes/additions of items shall be permitted unless approved, in writing, prior to the start of the Xth Annual [Event Name].

5. The health department, fire inspectors and Lessor shall have the legal right to inspect without notice. An authorized representative of Lessor shall have access to said premises at all times.

6. Concessionaire agrees to pay to Lessor with this registration/application the 10' wide x 20' long leased space deposit fee of $X,XXX with the remainder of the fee ($X,XXX) due and payable: a) online by credit card (details to be provided with acceptance of application) within time frame designated; or b) by check delivered to Xth Annual [Event Name] at [Physical and/or Mailing Address, City, State and Zip Code] on or before [Day of the Week, Month Date, 20XX] by [X:XX a.m./p.m.]

7. Concessionaire hereby consents and agrees that for any reason beyond the reasonable control of the Lessor, the Xth Annual [Event Name] is canceled in whole or in part, the Concessionaire's initial deposit would be non-refundable and that the Lessor would be relieved and released from any liability whatsoever for loss of business, expenses or any and all other claims which Concessionaire may have as a result of such cancellation. The leased space fee deposit will not be returned if Concessionaire cancels within 90 days prior to the start of the Xth Annual [Event Name].

8. Concessionaire shall furnish service on a fair, reasonable and non-discriminatory basis to all persons desiring such service. Concessionaire shall maintain and operate the concession in a first-class manner and shall keep the premises in a safe, clean, orderly and inviting condition at all times, satisfactory to Lessor.

9. Electricity will be provided by the [County/City/Venue] to the Lessor and equal access shall be provided to each of the Concessionaires. Each Concessionaire will pay Lessor a pro rata share of this expense. This expense has been included in the leased space fee for normal power consumption. Special electrical requirements will be billed to each Concessionaire. Normal power consumption will consist of not more than four (4) standard 110-plugs into power source provided. No electric generators will be permitted.

10. In addition to the leased space fees described in Paragraph 6 hereof, Concessionaire shall pay all other costs connected with the use of the premises and facilities, including, but not limited to, maintenance, insurance, any and all taxes, and all permits and licenses required by law. Concessionaire shall bear, at its own expense, all costs of operating the concession. Concessionaire will provide all equipment, for example, grills, sinks, ice chests, chaffing dishes, warming burners, furnishings, decorations, extension cords, supplies, like hand sanitizer, and fixtures, etc. Concession tent leased space; string lights; two (2), eight-foot long folding tables; and four (4) chairs will be assigned to Concessionaire by the Lessor. Loss or damage to the concession tent leased space, string lights, folding tables and/or chairs assigned will be the responsibility of the Concessionaire. All concession materials and equipment owned by Concessionaire shall be removed from [Venue/Location] by [X:XX a.m./p.m.] on the day AFTER closing of the Xth Annual [Event Name] and leased space shall be left in good, clean order.

11. Signs used by Concessionaire, must relate to Concessionaire's name, products or services normally offered by Concessionaire. Lessor reserves the right to require removal of unauthorized signs that fail to conform to the signage requirements. Concessionaire agrees to post prices of products being sold on a sign four-feet wide by two-feet high (4' x 2'), placed in the center of his/his/their leased space at a height approximately 10 feet (10'). This sign is to have easily-read block lettering for item descriptions and prices. Failure to post this sign and abide by such posted prices shall result in the Agreement being immediately canceled and Concessionaire shall vacate its location and leave [Venue/Location] prior to the next day's opening. An eight-foot wide by two-foot high (8' x 2') company/product identification sign will be allowed; it will be hung or placed over the booth by Lessor's designate. Concession signage showing product and prices must be delivered to the Xth Annual [Event Name] Concession Committee Chairman 14 days prior to the event's start date, so that it can be reviewed to insure it meets the requirements and so that Lessor's designee can prepare it to be properly hung in place.

12. Food Concessionaires with cooking facilities are required to follow all rules established by the local health department. Regulations requiring: a) proper disposal of grease and graywater; b) fire retardant grease mats when cooking on a grill or using fire (charcoal); c) a workable fire extinguisher in each of its leased spaces; and d) all decorations must be flame proofed and be approved by the health department.

13. Concessionaire to serve food and drinks in materials they supply, for example, cups, bowls, plates, knife, forks, spoons, etc. Only Concessionaire's logos shall appear on the serving items and packaging - not the event's, supplier's or third-party logos.

14. Lessor reserves the right to remove from [Venue/Location] any Concessionaire or any part thereof which Lessor deems objectionable. The Lessor agrees no refund of money paid for leased space will be made. If such action is taken, Concessionaire waives all claims whatsoever against the Lessor, its officers, employees or agents.

15. No sale or consumption of alcoholic beverages is permitted in [Venue/Location] during the Xth Annual [Event Name]. Concessionaire and its personnel are not permitted to consume alcohol during the event.

16. No solicitors or sales people will be allowed to work in the aisles or roadways. Concessionaire may advertise and display from within Concessionaire's leased space only. Concessionaire may not engage in any activities or demonstrations outside its leased space.

17. Promiscuous handing-out of any type of literature is not permitted, even from within Concessionaire's leased space. Such literature may be available on your counter and distributed only upon approval by Lessor.

18. No drawing or giveaway shall be conducted by Concessionaire unless the Xth Annual [Event Name] has given prior written permission.

19. No voice or sound amplifications shall be used by Concessionaire. No amateur or professional entertainment shall be used without consent of Lessor. Said permission, if granted, may be rescinded at any time by the Lessor.

20. Unbecoming conduct, to include the use of profane, obscene, abusive or threatening language, by Concessionaire and its personnel shall be grounds for termination of Agreement and immediate eviction of Concessionaire from [Venue/Location].

21. No dogs are permitted in [Venue/Location] on leash or otherwise, other than service dogs or police dogs.

22. The Concessionaire agrees not to assign or sub-lease any part of the space herein stated or to exhibit any merchandise or service other than that sold by Concessionaire and specified in this Agreement and further agrees the exhibit shall be of such quality as it will not distract from the Xth Annual [Event Name] or neighboring concessions.

23. All the terms, covenants and agreements contained herein shall be binding upon and shall inure to the benefit of successors and assigns of the respective parties hereto.

24. Concessionaire shall indemnify and save harmless Lessor against all loss, cost, expense or damage on account of any injury to persons or property arising out of or in connection with Concessionaire's operation of business on the premises, including but not limited to, attorney's fees and costs, including those incurred on any appeal.

25. Concessionaire understands the Lessor will not be responsible for any losses suffered by Concessionaire as a result of theft, property damage, vandalism, or otherwise, despite the fact that the Lessor will provide some minimal security. It will be Concessionaire's responsibility to maintain adequate insurance of its own and to adequately secure its own property to protect itself against such damages.

26. Concessionaire agrees to maintain adequate bodily injury and property damage liability insurance to protect itself and Lessor from any and all claims for injuries or property damage suffered as a result of Concessionaire's operations at the Xth Annual [Event Name]. Concessionaire will provide Certificates of Insurance for all such policies two (2) weeks prior to the event start date to the Lessor as evidence the Lessor has been included as a named insured in said policies.

27. In any action to enforce any provisions of this Agreement, the prevailing party shall be entitled to recover reasonable attorney fees and costs.

The above statements are agreed upon by acceptance of this document and I/we hereby agree to abide by the Concessionaire Agreement.

The attached Addendum A is a true and complete list and by my/our written or electronic signature hereon constitute my/our Agreement to be jointly and severally bound by the terms of this Agreement.

IN WITNESS WHEREOF, the parties have executed this contract the date and year first written above.

_____   _____
Witnesses   Concessionaire Signature

_____   _____
Witnesses   Print Name

                                                            _____
                                                            Mailing Address

                                                            _____
                                                            City, State and Zip Code

                                                            [Full Legal Event Name]

                                                            By: _____
                                                            Signature

                                                            _____
                                                            Authorized Representative Title

Note: A portion of the Registration/Application Form can be attached as Addendum A to the Concessionaire Agreement. The Concession Committee may accept the Product and Price List as presented or make modifications (usually after conferring with the applicant).

Addendum A - Concessionaire Agreement

The Concessionaire requests commercial leased space as follows:

Number of 10' Wide x 20' Long Spaces: _____

Product* and Price List: _____

_____

_____

_____

_____

_____

Concessionaire Legal Name: _____

Restaurant/Organization Name: _____

Concessionaire Name (to appear in promotional materials): _____

Contact Name: _____

Physical Address: _____

City: _____ State: _____ Zip Code: _____

Mailing Address: _____

City: _____ State: _____ Zip Code: _____

Contact Number: _____ Email address: _____

Cell Phone:_____ OK to send Texts to Cell: ☐ Yes   ☐ No

*Note: When planning your proposed menu, remember this is a "quick" turnaround event. Make sure the food you are planning to prepare can be fixed quickly and is easy to prepare. All final menu selections are subject to the approval of the local health department. You will not be allowed to serve any item that has not been first approved by the [Event Name] Concession Committee and the health department prior to the start of the event. There will be no exceptions.

Selection Letter

Xth Annual [Event Name]
Selection Letter - Paper Registration/Application Form

Date

[Contact Person and Title]
[Company Name]
[Mailing Address]
[City, State and Zip Code]

Dear [Name]:
Congratulations! Your company, restaurant and/or non-profit organization has been selected as one of the concessions for the Xth Annual [Event Name]. Among other criteria, your selection was based on the quality food product your registration/application form detailed you would be serving to the more than XX,XXX people expected at this year's event, scheduled for [Month Date to Date, 20XX]. Your approved menu items are as follows: XXXXX, XXXX, XXXX, XXXX and XXXX.

Please find enclosed your copy of the fully executed Concessionaire Agreement and Addendum. As a reminder, you previously paid a $X,XXX registration/application deposit fee for the 10' x 20' leased space under the concession tent which also includes string lights; two (2), eight-foot long folding tables; and four (4) chairs. Please note: minimal security is provided during the event.

Your balance is due and payable: a) online by credit card - https://www.securecreditcard.com or b) by check delivered to Xth Annual [Event Name] at [Physical and/or Mailing Address, City, State and Zip Code] on or before [Day of the Week, Month Date, 20XX] by [X:XX a.m./p.m.]

Because of the amount of planning required, a meeting of all concessions/vendors (attendance required) will soon be set. We will answer all your questions at that time.

Also please find attached a list of selected concessionaires with a contact name and phone number should you desire to coordinate efforts. This list does not include email addresses, as we have not been authorized to release these. We have indicated those individuals who will accept texts on their smartphones.

If you have any questions concerning the Concessionaire Agreement, please contact me at XXX-XXX-XXXX. Again, congratulations! I look forward to working with you this year.

Sincerely,

[Name]
Concession Committee Chairman
food@eventdomainname.com
XXX-XXX-XXXX

Enclosures: Agreement with Addendum
             List of Concessionaires

Thanks But No Thanks Letter

Xth Annual [Event Name]
Rejection Letter - Online Registration/Application Form

Date

[Contact Person and Title]
[Company Name]
[Mailing Address]
[City, State and Zip Code]

Dear [Name]:
Thank you for your interest in the Xth Annual [Event Name].

The Concession Committee has reviewed all the applications for this year's event and scored each based on the criteria detailed on the registration/application form: quality food product to be sold in your booth space and as it relates to all event offerings; reference checks based on quality, cleanliness, speed of service, adaptability to a special event, cooperation with volunteers or staff, responsiveness to deadlines and following instructions; suggested price points; and use of recycled packaging.

While we were impressed with your overall registration/application, others scored higher and as such you did not make the final selection this year. We encourage you to apply again next year.

As previously advised, your registration/application fee is being refunded. You will be receiving an email indicating the fee you paid online is being canceled or refunded. A second email will be sent after your refund (or credit) has been issued to your original form of payment.

Thank you again.

Sincerely,

[Name]
Concession Committee Chairman
food@eventdomainname.com
XXX-XXX-XXXX

Pre-Event Meeting Email

YOU ARE INVITED

Because of the amount of planning required to make all aspects of the Xth Annual [Event Name] run smoothly, a planning meeting has been scheduled with all participating concessionaires on

[Day of the Week, Month Day, 20XX] at [X:XX a.m./p.m.]
[Location], [Physical Address, City, State and Zip Code] and [Phone Number]

All logistical information will be answered at that time as key contacts will be available to address electrical or power sources and limitations, health department requirements, water and sewer access and garbage collection. We'll also discuss vehicle access before, during and after the event, concession area credentials, parking and parking passes, availability of ice, order forms for event tee shirts for your workers/volunteers and port-o-lets. We will also discuss the possibility of the event renting a refrigeration storage truck.

Concessionaire's Name: _____

Contact Name: _____

Contact Number: _____   Email address: _____

Cell Phone:_____   OK to send Texts to Cell: ☐ Yes   ☐ No

Please complete the information below and bring it to the meeting.
Note: If using an online registration system, reach out to the selected concessionaires and request the following information.

List Electrical Requirements

Wattage: _____

Voltage: _____

Type of equipment to be used during the event: _____

_____

List Insurance Information

Workers' compensation insurance provider: _____

Policy number: _____

Effective date: _____

Please send your organization's Certificate of Insurance to:
Concession Committee Chairman
[Event Name]
[Mailing Address]
[City, State and Zip Code]

It can also be scanned and emailed to: concessions@eventdomainname.com

Refrigerated Storage Truck
We would be interested in storing food products in a refrigeration storage truck, if one would be rented. I understand, we would be allowed to store products at our own risk, based on space availability.

☐ Yes   ☐ No

Tablecloth Orders
The event recommends X tablecloths per day, per table.

I understand I will be required to pay for these by cash or check at time of delivery or in advance online.

A separate email will be sent to those desiring to purchase tablecloths online.

☐ Yes   ☐ No   I would like to order X tablecloths at $XX each.

I prefer to pay by   ☐ Cash   ☐ Check   ☐ Online

Security Passes
Concessions/vendors are limited to X credentials per booth per day. These may be color-coded by day.

Please indicate the number of persons you plan to have working at your concession booth each day.
Note: Or set a limit per concession for the event.

> Set Up: _____
> Day #1:   _____
> Day #2:   _____
> Day #3:   _____
> Day #4:   _____
> Load Out: _____

Concessionaire Banners
The sign vendor creating the [Event Name] banners has offered to also create an eight-foot wide by two-foot high (8' x 2') banner for each concessionaire, if desired. These will have grommets placed on all four corners plus two on each of the longest edges. The sign vendor will install all banners on set-up day at no additional charge.

☐ Yes   ☐ No   I would like to purchase banner(s)/sign(s) at $XXX each.
                             Total booths: _____

                             Please send your logo directly to: name@signvendor.com
                             The following file type is required: four-color editable .eps file with fonts outlined.

☐ Yes   ☐ No   I will be providing my own sign and it will meet the size requirements stated above.
                             I understand the sign vendor will install all concessionaire banners.

Pre-Event Reminder

As you know, Xth Annual [Event Name] will kick off next [Day of the Week]. It will begin at 6:00 p.m. and concessionaires are required to be ready to go at 5:30 p.m.

Enclosed you will find a list (or a link to a list) of all concessionaires and their locations in the tents, as well as the location to pick up your two parking passes and concession area credentials for your workers/volunteers. These are available for pick up before [Day of the Week, Month Date] at [X:XX a.m./p.m.]

Please display your parking pass in the front windshield or on the dashboard of your vehicle. Remember you are being provided ONE parking space behind the concession tent during the event. The other parking permits will allow you into the restricted area for load in, replenishing supplies and load out only. No vehicular traffic is permitted after the official event start time each day.

The concessionaire credentials or wristbands will need to be worn by all individuals within your leased booth space and no other credentials or wristbands will be available so please use them sparingly.

To save time and make things as easy as possible, you will find key information below:

- The health department and fire inspectors have the legal right to inspect without notice and the event reserves the right to inspect, too.

- You may start setting up on opening day any time after [X:XX a.m./p.m.]

- All concessionaires are required by law to have one fire extinguisher per leased space.

- Concessionaires cooking on a grill or using fire (charcoal) are required to use fire retardant grease mats.

- The health department will remind concessionaires how grease and graywater (dirty water similar to household wastewater from sinks, showers, washing machines, bathtubs) needs to be properly disposed.

- We encourage each concessionaire to have well-charged mobile phones or to bring battery re-chargers to the event and have access to a power outlet.

- Be prepared to make change – lots of it. Remember: last year the [Do-Good Civic Association] went through $X,XXX worth of quarters during the event. Over prepare.

- Ice is available at the event in 50 lb. bags at a cost of $X.00 per bag, payable in cash at the end of the event. Do not leave the event until you have paid the Concession Committee Chairman or the Treasurer. A receipt will be issued at time of payment.

- If you ordered tablecloths, you will receive them on opening day during set up. You will be required to pay for them with cash or check at that time, providing you have not purchased them in advance online.

- Each concessionaire has been given a specific grouping of electrical plugs which have been labeled by number on the electrical panel. Your numbers will be emailed or sent as a text to you before [X:XX a.m./p.m.] tomorrow. Please use only your allotted number, as electricity is limited. No electric generators are permitted. Concessionaires are responsible for providing their own extension cords if needed.

- Banners will be hung by the event's sign vendor (even if not ordered through the vendor), so bring your banner as early as possible. The required dimensions are X' x X' and the banner should have grommets at all four corners plus two on each of the longest edges. The event will provide the rope for installation.

- The event, as part of your leased booth space, is providing string lights; two (2), eight-foot long folding tables; and four (4) chairs. You are directly responsible for these items. Failure to return them, and in clean condition, may result in additional charges. The event has limited security during the event for concessionaires.

- Due to the interest of concessionaires, the event has rented a refrigeration storage truck. Concessionaire can store products at their own risk, based on space availability. The Concession Committee Chairman will control the refrigeration truck key.

- The Agreement provides for all concessionaires to be open 30 minutes before the event until 30 minutes after the event each night. Please plan to be open during these times.

- A staff member of the local health department will be on hand to inspect your concession and issue permits, if approved, before [X:XX a.m./p.m.] on set-up day. Please have a member of your team available for the inspection.

Note: For events not using a flat fee concession agreement but, instead, using a flat fee plus an honor system - percentage of gross receipts, please add this bullet:

- Please make a list of food items by day with the exact quantity sold and return it to Xth Annual [Event Name] Treasurer by the Concessionaire Agreement's final payment date, along with a check payable to the [Event Name] for X percent of your gross sales or gross sales less sales tax.

Food Concession/Vendor Post-Event Survey

Thank you for participating in the Xth Annual [Event Name]. To assist us in making next year's event even better, please take a moment to complete this questionnaire.

Did the 20XX [Event Name] meet your expectations?   ☐ Yes ☐ No

If not, why not? _____

Do you feel your participation in this event was of financial or promotional benefit to your organization? ☐ Yes ☐ No

Does your organization have an interest in participating in next year's event?   ☐ Yes ☐ No

Would your organization have any interest in being a corporate sponsor of next year's event?   ☐ Yes ☐ No

Would a common on-site food preparation area be of any value to you as a vendor? (health dept. approved) ☐ Yes ☐ No

Please rate the following:

	Excellent	Good	Fair	Poor
Tents	☐	☐	☐	☐
Electrical	☐	☐	☐	☐
Water	☐	☐	☐	☐
Garbage	☐	☐	☐	☐
Banners	☐	☐	☐	☐
Event Assistance (for example, Concession Committee, ice, etc.)	☐	☐	☐	☐

Please provide additional comments where indicated for any area(s) you rate as poor.

_____

Please list positive points you feel helped make the event successful.

_____

Please list any areas you feel need to be addressed to improve the event.

_____

Please make any suggestions for changes or additions you feel are needed.

_____

Concessionaire's Name (optional): _____

Contact (optional): _____

Phone (optional): _____

Email (optional): _____

Thank you for sharing.

Post-Event Thank-You Letters

Letter to the Editor

Dear [Editor Name]:

On behalf of the Xth Annual [Event Name] Organizing Committee, I want to express our sincere appreciation to [this community or the greater XYZ area] for its overwhelming support.

As a result of the efforts of more than XXX community and corporate volunteers and the generous financial support of our sponsors, more than XX,XXX residents and visitors enjoyed X wonderful days of exciting [event theme type] in a picture-perfect setting.

The energy of the volunteers, the contributions of dollars and services by local businesses, and the support of the City of [Name] and its employees truly showcase [City Name] at its finest.

In addition to showing this community's spirit, the [Event Name] is proud to draw visitors from throughout [the area, region, nation and world] for this annual event while generating a positive economic impact on [City Name].

Copies of this year's popular poster [or this year's popular tee shirts] are still available for [holiday or special gift giving]. Your readers can place orders by mailing $XX (plus $X for postage, handling and taxes) to the [Event Name], [Mailing Address, City, State and Zip Code], or go online to our website, www.eventdomainname.com and click on Merchandise.

We are very proud to have enhanced various aspects of the festival this year. A special thank you to [Organization A] for all its effort with the [Related Event Name]; [Organization B] for showcasing the festival to businesses interested in relocating to XYZ County; [Organization C] in bringing X [travel agents, travel writers or travel bloggers] to the festival; [Organization D and Talent's name] for all their efforts with the Children's Workshop; [Organization E] for underwriting the colorful banners promoting the downtown and the festival; and to [Organization F] for organizing a [event theme type] [cruise or dinner].

Congratulations to XYZ High School student, [First and Last Name], who was the recipient of the [Event Name's] scholarship and best wishes as [he/she] furthers [his/her] [theme type] studies.

Before planning begins for the next year's [Event Name], we wanted to express our gratitude to the [Editor's Publication's Name] for its excellent coverage of the event. We truly appreciate your support and enthusiasm.

A very special thank you goes to our 20XX [Event Name] major sponsors: X, Y and Z, as well as to our contributing sponsors: M, N, O and P. As a result of their generosity, one of the [Region's Name]'s finest traditions, a free, family festival featuring a unique [theme kind] continues to grow.

Sincerely,

[Name]
Event Chairman, [Event Name] Organizing Committee

P.S. My personal thanks to the XX-volunteers who make up the [Event Name] Organizing Committee. It is because of their efforts in planning and coordinating the event that it runs so smoothly. Thank you.

Sponsors

Dear [Name]:

The Xth Annual [Event Name] Organizing Committee and the [Host or Presenting Organization] would like to join the more than XX,XXX people in attendance in thanking you for your generous support of the [Event Name].

This year's event was a wonderful combination of incredible weather, great food, stellar talent, a perfect setting and the largest crowd to ever attend the [Event Name]. As a corporate sponsor, you can be very proud of your participation in this major community event.

As this year draws to a close, we will soon begin planning for the 20XX event. Next year will bring further improvements to make the event even better. The Organizing Committee hopes you will continue to support [Event Name], not only financially, but again with volunteers and endless enthusiasm.

Once again, thank you for your sponsorship of [Event Name].

Sincerely,

[Name]
Event Chairman
[Event Name] Organizing Committee
chairman@eventdomainname.com
XXX-XXX-XXXX

Talent

Dear [Name]:

We wish to extend a personal note of thanks to you for sharing your talents with us. It was the professionalism of individuals like yourself who made our Xth Annual [Event Name] the success that it was. Without your cooperation, such an event would not have been possible.

If you have had a good experience, the [Event Name] Organizing Committee hopes that you will share your enthusiasm with others and become an ambassador at large for our event.

The [Event Name] intends to continue to showcase [event theme type] talent of the highest standard.

Thank you again for making the Xth Annual [Event Name] an outstanding success.

Sincerely,

[Name]	[Name]	[Name]
Event Chairman	Entertainment Committee Chairman	Talent/Programming Coordinator
chairman@eventdomainname.com	entertainment@eventdomainname.com	talent@eventdomainname.com
XXX-XXX-XXXX	XXX-XXX-XXXX	XXX-XXX-XXXX

Concessionaires

Dear [Name]:
On behalf of the [Event Name] Organizing Committee, we want to thank you for helping make the Xth Annual [Event Name] a success!

Because of your participation, more than XX,XXX visitors to [Venue/Location] enjoyed the [Region's Name] finest traditions - X days of [event theme type] and a wide variety of taste-tempting foods, all in a picture-perfect setting [or adjust copy to reflect weather conditions].

We trust your organization benefited from the excellent turnout and the media coverage the [Event Name] received. The enclosed article, based on a pre-event news release, features you and other concessionaires.

We hope you are as pleased with the results of the [Event Name] as we are. To assist us in making next year's event even better, please share your thoughts and suggestions with us by completing an online survey. [Concession Committee Chairman Name] will be sending you an email shortly with a link to this survey.

We truly appreciate your involvement with [Event Name] and look forward to working with you in the future.

Sincerely,

[Name]	[Name]	[Name]
Event Chairman	Site Services Committee Chairman	Concession Committee Chairman
chairman@eventdomainname.com	venue@eventdomainname.com	food@eventdomainname.com
XXX-XXX-XXXX	XXX-XXX-XXXX	XXX-XXX-XXXX

HELPFUL RESOURCES AND NOTES

FESTIVAL & EVENT ASSOCIATIONS by STATE and REGION

Arizona
Festival Event Association of Tucson and Southern Arizona
http://featsaz.com

Arkansas
Arkansas Festivals and Events Association
http://www.arfea.org

California
California/Nevada Festivals and Events Association
http://www.calfest.org

Colorado
Colorado Festivals and Events Association
http://coloradofestival.com

Florida
Florida Festival and Events Association
http://www.ffea.com

Greater Miami Festivals and Events
http://www.FestivalsMiami.com

Illinois
International Live Events Association
http://www.ileahub.com

Indiana
Indiana Festivals
http://www.indianafestivals.org

Kansas
Kansas Fairs and Festivals Association
http://www.kansasfairsassociation.com

Kentucky
Kentucky Festivals and Events Association
http://kfea.com

Louisiana
Louisiana Association of Fairs and Festivals
http://www.laffnet.org

Michigan
Michigan Festivals and Events Association
http://www.mfea.org

Minnesota
Minnesota Festivals and Events Association
http://www.mnfea.com

Missouri
Missouri Association of Fairs and Festivals
http://www.mofairs.org

Nevada
California/Nevada Festivals and Events Association
http://www.calfest.org

North Carolina
North Carolina Association of Festivals and Events
http://ncfestivals.com

Ohio
Ohio Festivals and Events Association
http://ofea.org

Oregon
Oregon Festival and Events Association
http://www.oregonfestivals.org

South Carolina
South Carolina Festival and Event Association
http://scfea.com

Texas
Texas Festivals and Events Association
http://www.tfea.org

Utah
Utah Association of Fairs and Events
http://www.utahfairsandevents.org

Washington
Washington Festivals and Events Association
http://www.wfea.org

West Virginia
West Virginia Association of Fairs and Festivals
http://www.wvfairsandfestivals.org

Southeast U.S.
Southeast Festival and Events Association
http://www.southeastfestivals.org

International
International Festivals and Events Association
http://www.ifea.com

Canada
Festivals and Events Prince Edward Island
http://www.festivalspei.com

Festivals and Events Ontario
http://www.festivalsandeventsontario.ca

Ottawa Festivals
http://www.ottawafestivals.ca

Ireland
Association of Irish Festivals and Events
http://www.aoifeonline.com

United Kingdom
The Association of Festival Organisers
http://www.festivalorganisers.org

National Outdoor Events Associations
http://www.noea.org.uk

FOOD, BEER, WINE & SPIRITS ORGANIZATIONS

American Brewers Guild
http://abgbrew.com

American Homebrewers Association
http://www.homebrewersassociation.org

American Institute of Wine and Food
http://www.aiwf.org

Brewers Association
https://www.brewersassociation.org

National Food Truck Association
http://www.nationalfoodtrucks.org

National Restaurant Association
http://www.restaurant.org

Wine and Spirits Wholesalers of America
http://www.wswa.org

WineAmerica
http://wineamerica.org

Wine Institute
http://www.wineinstitute.org

Wine Market Council
http://winemarketcouncil.com

World Food Travel Association
https://worldfoodtravel.org

MUSIC LICENSING

Broadcast Music, Inc.®
http://www.bmi.com
Music Users > Licensing
877-264-2137 | 888-689-5264

The American Society of Composers, Authors and Publishers (ASCAP)
http://www.ascap.com

ORGANIZATIONS

Main Street America™
http://www.preservationnation.org/main-street

National Recreation and Park Association
http://www.nrpa.org/

SUPPLIERS

American Pyrotechnics Association
http://www.americanpyro.com

National Fireworks Association
http://www.nationalfireworks.org

Drum Corps International
http://www.dci.org

National Independent Concessionaires Association, Inc.
http://www.nicainc.org

**International Amusement
& Leisure Defense Association**
http://www.ialda.org

Portable Sanitation Association International
http://www.PSAI.org

Mid America Horse Show Association
http://www.midamericahorseshow.org

NOTES

QR Code is a trademark of DENSO WAVE INCORPORATED CORPORATION JAPAN in the U.S. and other countries.

TWITTER, TWEET, RETWEET and the Twitter logo are trademarks of Twitter, Inc. or its affiliates.

Acknowledgments

An enormous thank you to my husband for his love and encouragement. To our boys who remind me daily when it's time to leave my office and go home.

With deep appreciation to those:

- Who have inspired: Gertrude Brainerd, Joann Dumont, Irene Obrecht Estes and Mary Ann Young.

- Who saw promise, mentored and inspired: Nancy Kaylor.

- Who has led, made footprints, allowed me to walk in them and add a few of my own: Nancy Kaylor.

- Who were always up for a challenge and said yes when asked: Fred Boscarino, Bruce Boyers, Dale Kleine, Claude Miranda, Valarie Nussbaum-Harris, Victoria Scotti and Deborah Vincent. Plus a host of others too numerous to mention.

- Who have never said no: Anne Adams, Ron Bortolini and Ebe Bower.

- Who were always there ... Anthony & Julia, Cathy, Cheryl, Dale, Ebe, Francis, Joseph & Deb, Nancy & Steve, Nancy & Ray, Patrick and Todd.

To my family ... dad, mom and my siblings, especially my brother John, Cousin Barb and Aunt Mary, Aunt Adrienne and Uncle Ralph for the foundation of love and support they have given me and continue to do so today.

About the Author

Throughout her career, Lynn Fuhler has successfully organized and promoted numerous festivals as well as corporate and community events and leadership programs and activities. The former Tourism and Convention Director of Clearwater and Clearwater Beach, Fla., currently the #1 beach destination in the United States, has worked extensively with the hospitality industry to market destinations, festivals, events and visitor activities throughout the world. She is the former Event Chairman of the all-volunteer Clearwater Jazz Holiday, then the largest free jazz festival in the Southeast U.S.

Lynn Fuhler is a consultant, speaker and publisher of a blog which focuses on all aspects of festival and event planning. A native of Illinois and the greater St. Louis area, Lynn holds a B.S. degree in transportation, travel and tourism from St. Louis University's Parks College. Based in North Carolina, Lynn is the co-founder of Flying Compass, Inc. a hospitality marketing company.

A Midwesterner at heart, Fuhler resided in Florida for many years before heading to the Carolinas. Travel is her avocation, along with studying maps, people and places. She credits newspaper advice columns she read while growing up with helping her hone her problem solving skills. She has fond memories of camping which laid the foundation for festival and event management.

www.lynnfuhler.com
www.festivalexperts.org

Other Publications by Lynn Fuhler:

Secrets to Successful Events:
How to Organize, Promote and Manage Exceptional Events and Festivals

Made in the
USA
Middletown, DE